THE THEORY OF OPTIMUM NOISE IMMUNITY

by V. A. Kotel'nikov

TRANSLATED FROM THE RUSSIAN

by R. A. Silverman

INSTITUTE OF MATHEMATICAL SCIENCES
NEW YORK UNIVERSITY

McGRAW-HILL BOOK COMPANY, INC.
New York Toronto London
1959

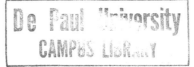

THE THEORY OF OPTIMUM NOISE IMMUNITY

 Library of Congress Catalog Card Number 59-9990

35346

AUTHOR'S PREFACE

This book is the author's doctoral dissertation, presented in January, 1947, before the academic council of the Molotov Energy Institute in Moscow. Despite the fact that many works devoted to noise immunity have appeared in the time that has elapsed since the writing of this dissertation, not all of the topics considered in it have as yet appeared in print. Considering the great interest shown in these matters, and also the number of references made to this work in the literature, the author has deemed it appropriate to publish it, without introducing any supplementary material. However, in preparing the manuscript for publication, it was somewhat condensed, at the expense of material of secondary interest. Moreover, Chapter 2, which contains auxiliary mathematical material, has been revised somewhat, to make it easier reading, and some of the material has been relegated to the appendices.

The author

EXPLANATORY NOTE

The study of probability theory and its applications has had a long and illustrious history in Russia, beginning in the earliest days of the 18th century, and continuing in an unbroken line down to the present generation. In our time we have seen a realization that in many aspects of science, technology, and human behavior the element of randomness is so fundamental that often one can hardly define a meaningful problem, much less solve it, without using probability theory. During the rapid technological developments of the World War II period, the communication and detection arts underwent such a realization, and as would be expected, statistical communication theory (or information theory) has occupied some of the best minds among mathematicians and engineers in the Soviet Union just as it has elsewhere.

One of the most important Soviet contributions, and one that was until recently virtually unknown outside the U.S.S.R., was the 1947 doctoral dissertation of V. A. Kotel'nikov, at that time a 40-year-old communications engineer, who had already in his younger days (1933) become well known for his work on sampling theorems for band-limited functions. Kotel'nikov's dissertation constituted an extensive analysis of the effects of additive gaussian noise on communication systems, and of what could be done at the receiver to minimize them. Unlike Shannon's information theory, he did not go extensively into the implications of a freedom to choose complicated transmitter signals.

Many Soviet contributions to the statistical communication art are fairly well known to us. Every student of these matters knows the names Khinchin and Kolmogorov as partners with Western mathematicians (notably Norbert Wiener) in the early development of spectral and filtering theories for random functions. Yet few of us have been aware that there existed in 1947 in this dissertation a statistical analysis of communication problems using what we now call decision theory techniques and anticipating by several years much of the work of Woodward, Davies, Siegert and others, with which we are more conversant.

This book is a verbatim translation of "The Theory of Potential Noise Immunity", published by the State Power Engineering Press in 1956. As the Author's Preface has just indicated, it is essentially identical to the 1947 dissertation. In preparing this English edition, no technical editing has been done other than the correction of misprints. The present volume thus retains the exact flavor of the original, allowing one to see from hindsight which of Kotel'nikov's many highly original ideas have been developed further and which have not.

By no means all of Kotel'nikov's results have since been obtained independently by others, and thus the volume should be of much more than just historical interest.

Perhaps the reader will be aided by the following few comments which should make the unfamiliar terminology a little easier to follow, and should clarify the relationship between this and other works in the communication theory field.

First of all there is the question of just what is meant by "noise immunity". As used here, it is a generic term with a different meaning for different situations. For Part II, the case in which communication takes place by transmitting one out of a finite number of possible signals the term refers to probability of no error. (Part II discusses what we would now call the "multiple-alternative decision" problem.) Part III treats the situation in which a continuum of transmitted signals is assumed (a parameter λ ranging over some interval taking the place of the previous discrete index of the possible signals); i.e., the problem of "parameter estimation". Here a greater noise immunity refers to a decrease in mean square value of the error between the value of λ indicated by the receiver and that actually transmitted. And then when the author treats in Part IV the case of signalling using waveforms (the parameter now being replaced by a function of time in some time interval) an increased noise immunity refers to a decrease in the average noise power that additively corrupts the receiver output. In other words, the author is dealing with the mean-square error between the modulating signal entering the transmitter, and that reproduced by the receiver. Note that the author never says that noise immunity "is" one of these three things, but rather "is characterized by" one of them. This usage persists in the large number of Soviet papers that have continued Kotel'nikov's work.

The development presented here is notable in its absence of any dependence on an advanced mathematical background. The reader possessing a passing familiarity with Fourier series, discrete and continuous probabilities and probability densities (simple, joint, and conditional) and the notion of statistical independence will have no trouble. At several points some known results of probability theory are invoked without reference or proof. (One that the beginning reader might not be familiar with is the Central Limit Theorem, Equation 2-33.) However, these instances are rare; by and large the treatment is completely self-sufficient.

Kotel'nikov made extensive use of geometric models of the signalling and detection processes as operations on vectors in multi-dimensional space, an artifice that Shannon introduced later. The reader will find these geometric interpretations very helpful. The material of each chapter is reviewed in terms of the geometric model at the end of the chapter.

Paul E. Green, Jr.
M.I.T. Lincoln Laboratory

TABLE OF CONTENTS

CHAPTER 4

NOISE IMMUNITY FOR SIGNALS WITH TWO DISCRETE VALUES

CHAPTER 5

NOISE IMMUNITY FOR SIGNALS WITH MANY DISCRETE VALUES

PART III

TRANSMISSION OF SEPARATE PARAMETER VALUES

CHAPTER 6

GENERAL THEORY OF THE INFLUENCE OF NOISE ON THE TRANSMISSION OF SEPARATE PARAMETER VALUES

CHAPTER 7

THE OPTIMUM NOISE IMMUNITY OF VARIOUS SYSTEMS FOR TRANSMITTING SEPARATE PARAMETER VALUES IN THE PRESENCE OF LOW INTENSITY NOISE

CHAPTER 8

NOISE IMMUNITY FOR TRANSMISSION OF SEPARATE PARAMETER VALUES IN THE PRESENCE OF STRONG NOISE

PART IV

TRANSMISSION OF WAVEFORMS

CHAPTER 9

GENERAL THEORY OF THE INFLUENCE OF WEAK NOISE ON THE TRANSMISSION OF WAVEFORMS

CHAPTER 10

DIRECT MODULATION SYSTEMS

CHAPTER 11

PULSE MODULATION SYSTEMS

CHAPTER 12

INTEGRAL MODULATION SYSTEMS

CHAPTER 13

EVALUATION OF THE INFLUENCE OF STRONG NOISE ON THE TRANSMISSION OF WAVEFORMS

APPENDICES

PART I
AUXILIARY MATERIAL

CHAPTER 1
INTRODUCTION

1-1 Methods of combating noise

Ordinarily, a radio receiver is acted upon not only by disturbances (signals) produced by the radio transmitter, but also by disturbances (noise) produced by a large variety of sources. The noise combines with the signals and corrupts them; in the case of telegraphic reception this leads to errors, and in the case of telephonic reception to background noise, static, etc. When the signals are too small compared to the noise, reception becomes impossible.

The following methods of combating noise are used:

1. Decreasing the strength of the noise by taking action against their sources.
2. Increasing the ratio of the strength of the signals to that of the noise by increasing the transmitter power and by using directional antennas.
3. Improving the receivers.
4. Changing the form of the signals while keeping their power fixed. (This is done with the aim of facilitating the combating of noise in the receiver.)

The first two methods are not considered in this book, which is devoted rather to the last two methods, and has as its goal to examine whether it is possible to decrease the effect of noise by improving the receivers, given the existing kinds of signals. In particular, what can be achieved in combating noise by changing the form of the signals? What form of signals is optimum for this purpose?

1-2 Classification of noise

We can classify the noise which impedes radio reception into the following categories:

A. Sinusoidal noise consisting of one or a finite number (usually small) of sinusoidal oscillations. This category of noise includes interference from the parasitic radiation of one or more radio stations operating at frequencies near that of the station being received.

B. Impulse noise consisting of separate impulses which follow one another at such large time intervals that the transients produced in the receiver by one impulse have substantially died out by the time the next impulse arrives. This category of noise includes some kinds of atmospheric noise and noise from electrical apparatus.

C. Normal fluctuation noise[1] or, as it is sometimes called, smoothed-out noise. This also consists of separate impulses, occurring at random time intervals, but the impulses follow one another so rapidly that the transients produced in the receiver by the individual impulses are superimposed in numbers large enough to warrant the application of the laws of large numbers of probability theory. This category of noise includes vacuum tube noise, noise due to the thermal motion of electrons in circuits, and some kinds of atmospheric noise and noise from electrical apparatus. At very high frequencies this kind of noise is encountered almost exclusively.

D. Impulse noise of an intermediate type, which occurs when the transients produced in the receiver by the individual impulses are superimposed, but not in numbers large enough to warrant the application with sufficient accuracy of the laws of large numbers. This kind of noise is intermediate between categories B and C.

Methods of studying the action of sinusoidal and impulse noise on radio receivers are at present quite well developed. The study of impulse noise of the intermediate type, when the transients produced by the individual impulses are just beginning to be superimposed, is much more difficult. Moreover, in this case, we need to know not only the shapes of the separate impulses, but also the probability of superposition of impulses which have various shapes, and which obey various time distributions. In most cases we do not have this information about the noise, and it seems to be quite difficult to obtain. For these reasons, and also because noise of category C is often encountered, in what follows we shall consider only noise of this latter category; we shall often designate normal fluctuation noise simply as noise.

1-3 Messages and signals

By a message we shall mean that which is to be transmitted. The messages with which we shall be concerned can be divided into three categories.

A. Discrete messages.

B. Messages in the form of separate numbers (parameters), which can take on any values in certain ranges.

C. Messages in the form of wave trains, which can assume a continuous infinity of different waveforms.

The messages which are transmitted in telegraphy belong to the category of discrete messages. In this case, they consist of discrete letters, numerals, and characters, which can take on a finite number of discrete values. Moreover, in many instances, the messages transmitted in remote-control systems belong to this category.

---

1. The use of the word "normal" alludes to the fact that we deal here with one of a variety of possible fluctuation processes.

In the case of the transmission of individual measurements with the aid of telemetering, the messages consist of the values of certain parameters (e.g., temperature, pressure, etc.) measured at given time intervals. These quantities usually take on arbitrary values lying within certain ranges. Thus, in this case we cannot restrict ourselves to a finite number of possible discrete messages. Messages of this kind belong to category B.

In the case of telephony, the messages are acoustical vibrations, or the electrical vibrations taking place in the microphone, which can take on an infinite number of different forms. These messages belong to category C. In television, the oscillations acting on the transmitter can be taken as the message; this message also belongs to the last category.

We shall assume that some variation in voltage, produced by the operation of the transmitter, acts upon the receiver input. We have called this variation in voltage a signal. Clearly, there will be a signal corresponding to each possible transmitted message. The receiver must use this voltage waveform (i.e., signal) to reproduce the message to which the signal corresponds.

1-4 The contents of this book

In this book we consider the influence of normal fluctuation noise on the transmission of messages. The problem which will concern us is the following: We assume that when the noise perturbation is not superimposed on the signal, then the receiver will reproduce the transmitted message exactly. If noise is added to the signal, then the sum of two voltages will act upon the receiver input, i.e., the signal voltage plus the noise voltage. In this case, depending on the sum voltage, the receiver will reproduce some message or other, which in a given instance may be different from the one that was transmitted. Clearly, each sum voltage which acts upon the receiver produces the particular message which corresponds to it. This correspondence may be different for different receivers. Depending on this correspondence, a receiver will be more or less subject to the influence of noise for a given kind of transmission. We shall find out what this correspondence ought to be for the message corruption to be the least possible. The receiver which has this optimum correspondence will be called ideal.

Next we shall determine the message perturbation which results when noise is added to the signals, and when the reception is with an ideal receiver; the message perturbation obtained in this way will be the least possible under the given conditions, i.e., for real receivers under the same conditions, the message perturbation cannot be less. The noise immunity characterized by this least possible message perturbation will be called the optimum noise immunity. This noise immunity can be approached in real receivers if the receiver is close to being ideal, but it cannot be exceeded. By comparing the optimum noise immunity with the noise immunity afforded by real receivers, we can judge how close the latter are to perfection, and how much the noise immunity can be increased by improving them, i.e., to what extent it is advisable to work on further increasing the noise immunity for a given means of communication. Knowledge of the optimum noise immunity makes it easy to discover and reject methods of communication for which this noise immunity is low compared with other methods. This can be done without reference to the method of reception, since real receivers cannot achieve noise immunity greater than the optimum. By comparing the optimum noise immunity for different means of communication, we can easily explain (as will be seen subsequently) the basic factors on which the immunity depends, and thereby increase the immunity by changing the means of communication. In the book, these matters are illustrated by a whole series of examples which have practical interest. However, the examples considered are far from exhausting all possible cases in which one can apply the methods of studying noise immunity developed here.

In the book, all questions are discussed in connection with radio reception, in the interest of greater clarity; however, all that is said is directly applicable to other fields, like, for example, cable communication, acoustical and hydroacoustical signaling, etc. Moreover, in the book, all signal and noise disturbances are considered to be oscillations of voltage; however, nothing is changed if we consider instead oscillations of current, acoustical pressure, or of any other quantity which characterizes the disturbance acting on the receiver.

This book does not consider certain irregular perturbations of the signals, which can strongly affect both the operation of radio receivers and their noise immunity. Examples of such perturbations are fading, echo phenomena, etc. Moreover, it should be kept in mind that in this book the word noise is henceforth (for brevity) understood to refer to normal fluctuation noise; indeed, this is the only kind of noise which will be considered.

CHAPTER 2
AUXILIARY MATHEMATICAL MATERIAL

2-1 Some definitions

We now introduce some definitions which simplify the subsequent analysis. We assume that all waveforms under consideration lie in the interval $-T/2, +T/2$, which is obviously always the case for sufficiently large T.

The mean value of a waveform $A(t)$ over the interval T is designated by

$$\overline{A(t)} = \frac{1}{T} \int_{-T/2}^{+T/2} A(t)\, dt \tag{2-1}$$

By the scalar product of two functions $A(t)$ and $B(t)$, we understand the mean value of their product over the interval $-T/2, +T/2$. Thus, the scalar product is

$$\overline{A(t)\, B(t)} = \frac{1}{T} \int_{-T/2}^{+T/2} A(t)\, B(t)\, dt \tag{2-2}$$

It is clear from the definition that

$$\overline{A(t)\, B(t)} = \overline{B(t)\, A(t)} \tag{2-3}$$

Furthermore

$$\overline{A(t)\, [B(t) + C(t)]} = \overline{A(t)\, B(t)} + \overline{A(t)\, C(t)} \tag{2-4}$$

and

$$\overline{[aA(t)]\, [bB(t)]} = ab\, \overline{A(t)\, B(t)} \tag{2-5}$$

where a and b are arbitrary constants. Thus, the scalar product of functions has the same properties as the scalar product of vectors; instead of scalars we have constants, and instead of vectors we have functions.

We write

$$\overline{A^2(t)} = \overline{A(t)\, A(t)} = \frac{1}{T} \int_{-T/2}^{+T/2} A^2(t)\, dt \tag{2-6}$$

In what follows, we shall often encounter the quantity

$$T\, \overline{A^2(t)} = \int_{-T/2}^{+T/2} A^2(t)\, dt \tag{2-7}$$

This quantity will be called the specific energy of the waveform A(t). It equals the energy expended in a resistance of 1 ohm acted upon by the voltage A(t). The quantity

$$\sqrt{\overline{A^2(t)}} \tag{2-8}$$

will be called the effective value of the waveform A(t). A function with effective value unity is said to be normalized.

If two functions differ only by a constant, they are said to coincide in direction. The normalized function which coincides in direction with a given function A(t) is obviously

$$\frac{A(t)}{\sqrt{\overline{A^2(t)}}} \tag{2-9}$$

We shall say that the functions $A_1(t), A_2(t), \ldots, A_n(t)$ are (mutually) orthogonal, if

$$\overline{A_i(t)\, A_\ell(t)} = 0 \tag{2-10}$$

for all $1 \leq i, \ell \leq n$, except when $i = \ell$.

2-2 Representation of a function as a linear combination of orthonormal functions

If the system of functions

$$C_1(t), C_2(t), \ldots, C_n(t) \tag{2-11}$$

satisfies the equations

$$\overline{C_k^2(t)} = 1 \tag{2-12}$$

$$\overline{C_k(t)\, C_\ell(t)} = 0 \tag{2-13}$$

where $1 \leq k, \ell \leq n$ and $k \neq \ell$, we say that it is a system of orthonormal functions. An example of such a system of functions is the system

$$\begin{aligned}
I_0(t) &= 1, \\
I_1(t) &= \sqrt{2} \sin \frac{2\pi}{T} t, \\
I_2(t) &= \sqrt{2} \cos \frac{2\pi}{T} t, \\
I_3(t) &= \sqrt{2} \sin 2 \frac{2\pi}{T} t, \\
I_4(t) &= \sqrt{2} \cos 2 \frac{2\pi}{T} t., \\
&\cdots\cdots \\
I_{2m-1}(t) &= \sqrt{2} \sin m \frac{2\pi}{T} t, \\
I_{2m}(t) &= \sqrt{2} \cos m \frac{2\pi}{T} t,
\end{aligned} \tag{2-14}$$

since for this system the relations

$$\overline{I_k^2(t)} = 1, \quad \overline{I_k(t)\, I_\ell(t)} = 0 \qquad (k \neq \ell) \tag{2-15}$$

are valid. We shall say that a function $A(t)$ can be represented as a linear combination of a system of functions

$$C_1(t),\ C_2(t),\ \ldots\ ,\ C_n(t) \tag{2-16}$$

if we can write

$$A(t) = \sum_{k=1}^{n} a_k C_k(t) \tag{2-17}$$

where some of the a_k may vanish.

If we assume that the functions (2-16) are orthonormal, then, taking the scalar product of both sides of Eq. (2-17) with $C_\ell(t)$ and expanding, we obtain, with the use of Eqs. (2-12) and (2-13)

$$\overline{A(t)\ C_\ell(t)} = a_\ell \tag{2-18}$$

We call the coefficients a_k the coordinates of the function $A(t)$ in the system (2-16). Obviously, the function $A(t)$ is completely characterized by the n coordinates $a_1, \ldots, a_n$, if the system (2-16) is specified. In particular, if we take as the system of orthonormal functions the system (2-14), we obtain

$$A(t) = \sum_{\ell=0}^{\infty} a_\ell I_\ell(t) \tag{2-19}$$

where

$$a_\ell = \overline{A(t)\ I_\ell(t)} \tag{2-20}$$

The series (2-19) is the familiar expansion of the function $A(t)$ as a Fourier series in the interval $-T/2, +T/2$. According to (2-14), the amplitude of the cosine term of frequency m/T is $\sqrt{2}\ a_{2m}$, and the amplitude of the corresponding sine term is $\sqrt{2}\ a_{2m-1}$.

If the oscillation $A(t)$ is a signal, then we usually only consider a finite number of terms of the sum (2-19), with indices from ℓ_1 to ℓ_2, say, since the components of the signal are as a rule so small outside a certain frequency range that they are masked by noise or by the components of other signals being transmitted on neighboring frequencies. In this case

$$A(t) = \sum_{\ell=\ell_1}^{\ell_2} a_\ell I_\ell(t) \tag{2-21}$$

Let $a_1, \ldots, a_n$ be the coordinates of the function $A(t)$ in the system (2-16) and let $b_1, \ldots, b_n$ be the coordinates of the function $B(t)$ in the same system. Then

$$\overline{A(t)\ B(t)} = \overline{\left[\sum_{k=1}^{n} a_k C_k(t)\right]\left[\sum_{k=1}^{n} b_k C_k(t)\right]} = \sum_{k=1}^{n} a_k b_k \tag{2-22}$$

which follows easily by expanding and using Eqs. (2-12) and (2-13). As a special case, we have

$$\overline{A^2(t)} = \overline{A(t)\,A(t)} = \sum_{k=1}^{n} a_k^2 \qquad (2\text{-}23)$$

If $C(t)$ is a normalized function with coordinates $c_1, \ldots, c_n$, then

$$\sum_{k=1}^{n} c_k^2 = 1 \qquad (2\text{-}24)$$

Furthermore, if the functions $A(t)$ and $B(t)$ are orthogonal, then according to the formula (2-22) and the orthogonality condition (2-10), we have

$$\sum_{k=1}^{n} a_k b_k = \overline{A(t)\,B(t)} = 0 \qquad (2\text{-}25)$$

The expressions (2-22), (2-23), and (2-25) are the analogs of the corresponding expressions of vector analysis.

Finally, we show that if two functions

$$A(t) = \sum_{k=o}^{n} a_k I_k(t)$$

$$B(t) = \sum_{k=o}^{n} b_k I_k(t)$$

have no components with identical frequencies, i.e., if for all indices $k \neq 0$, either one of the a_k or one of the b_k is zero, then

$$\overline{A(t)\,B(t)} = \overline{A(t)}\;\overline{B(t)} \qquad (2\text{-}26)$$

Indeed, under these conditions

$$\overline{A(t)\,B(t)} = a_o b_o$$

and furthemore

$$\overline{A(t)} = a_o, \qquad \overline{B(t)} = b_o$$

whence Eq. (2-20) follows at once.

2-3 Normal fluctuation noise

We shall consider noise consisting of a large number of short pulses, randomly distributed in time. Such noise will be called normal fluctuation noise. This kind of noise includes thermal noise in conductors, shot noise in vacuum tubes, and, in many cases, atmospheric and man-made noise as well. Such a noise process can be represented by the expression

$$W(t) = \sum_{k=1}^{n} F_k(t-t_k) \tag{2-27}$$

where $F_k(t-t_k)$ is the k'th pulse occurring in the interval $-T/2, +T/2$. We assume that the pulses are short and begin at the times t_k. Thus

$$F_k(t-t_k) = 0 \qquad \text{for} \quad t < t_k \text{ and } t > t_k + \delta \tag{2-28}$$

Here the pulses are to be numbered by the indices k not in the order of their occurrence in time, but (say) in order of decreasing amplitude.

Suppose that the probability of t_k falling in a subinterval of length dt is dt/T, and that it does not depend on the location of the subinterval within the interval $-T/2, +T/2$ nor on the other pulses. Moreover suppose that $\overline{A(t)} = 0$. Then we find that

$$\overline{W(t)\,A(t)} = \frac{1}{T} \int_{-T/2}^{+T/2} \sum_{k=1}^{n} F_k(t-t_k)\, A(t)\, dt = \sum_{k=1}^{n} \xi_k \tag{2-29}$$

where

$$\xi_k = \frac{1}{T} \int_{-T/2}^{+T/2} F_k(t-t_k)\, A(t)\, dt \tag{2-30}$$

Assuming that δ is so small that A(t) changes negligibly in the time δ, we obtain

$$\xi_k = \frac{A(t_k)}{T} \int_{t_k}^{t_k+\delta} F_k(t-t_k)\, dt = \frac{A(t_k)}{T} q_k \tag{2-31}$$

where

$$q_k = \int_0^{\delta} F_k(t)\, dt \tag{2-32}$$

is the area of the k'th pulse.

The summands ξ_k are mutually independent random variables. If they are bounded, and if the sum of their variances increases without limit as the number of summands is increased, then, according to probability theory, we obtain in the limit of infinite n

$$\lim \frac{\sum_{k=1}^{n} \xi_k - \sum_{k=}^{n} E\xi_k}{\sqrt{\sum_{k=1}^{n} D\xi_k}} = \theta_A \tag{2-33}$$

where $E\xi_k$ is the mean value, and $D\xi_k = E(\xi_k - E\xi_k)^2$ is the variance of the quantity ξ_k; θ_k is the random variable with distribution law

$$P(x < \theta_A < x + dx) = \frac{1}{\sqrt{2\pi}} e^{-x^2/2} dx \qquad (2-34)$$

In what follows, random variables with the distribution law (2-34) will be called normal random variables.

It follows from (2-33) that for sufficiently large n we can write

$$\overline{W(t)\ A(t)} = \sum_{k=1}^{n} \xi_k = \theta_A \sqrt{\sum_{k=1}^{n} D\xi_k} + \sum_{k=1}^{n} E\xi_k \qquad (2-35)$$

Moreover, by (2-31)

$$E\xi_k = \int_{-T/2}^{+T/2} \frac{q_k}{T} A(t_k) \frac{dt_k}{T} = q_k \frac{\overline{A(t)}}{T} = 0 \qquad (2-36)$$

since by assumption $\overline{A(t)} = 0$. We have also

$$D\xi_k = E(\xi_k - E\xi_k)^2 = \int_{-T/2}^{+T/2} \frac{q_k^2}{T^2} A^2(t_k) \frac{dt_k}{T} = \frac{q_k^2}{T^2} \overline{A^2(t)} \qquad (2-37)$$

whence

$$\overline{W(t)\ A(t)} = \frac{1}{T}\sqrt{\overline{A^2(t)} \sum_{k=1}^{n} q_k^2}\ \theta_A \qquad (2-38)$$

We shall call the quantity

$$\sigma = \sqrt{\frac{2 \sum_{k=1}^{n} q_k^2}{T}} \qquad (2-39)$$

the intensity of the process W(t). Thus we have

$$\overline{W(t)\ A(t)} = \frac{\sigma}{\sqrt{2T}} \sqrt{\overline{A^2(t)}}\ \theta_A \qquad (2-40)$$

We note that since the sum $\sum_{k=1}^{n} q_k^2$ is proportional to T, the quantity σ does not depend on T.

We now find $\overline{W(t)\ B(t)}$, assuming that

$$\overline{B(t)} = 0 \quad \text{and} \quad \overline{A(t)\ B(t)} = 0 \qquad (2-41)$$

In a way analogous to the above, we obtain

$$\overline{W(t)\ B(t)} = \sum_{k=1}^{n} \chi_k \qquad (2-42)$$

where

$$\chi_k = \frac{B(t_k)}{T} q_k \tag{2-43}$$

and

$$\overline{W(t)\, B(t)} = \frac{\sigma}{\sqrt{2T}} \sqrt{\overline{B^2(t)}}\ \theta_B \tag{2-44}$$

Here θ_B is a normal random variable which, like θ_A, satisfies Eq. (2-34). As shown in probability theory, $\sum_{k=1}^{n} \xi_k$ and $\sum_{k=1}^{n} \chi_k$ are independent random variables in the limit $n \to \infty$, provided that

$$E \xi_k \chi_k = 0 \tag{2-45}$$

Since we have

$$E \xi_k \chi_k = \int_{-T/2}^{+T/2} \frac{q_k^2}{T^2} A(t_k)\, B(t_k) \frac{dt_k}{T} = \frac{q_k^2}{T^2} \frac{1}{T} \int_{-T/2}^{+T/2} A(t_k)\, B(t_k)\, dt_k$$

$$= \frac{q_k^2}{T^2} \overline{A(t)\, B(t)} = 0 \tag{2-46}$$

it follows that the quantities θ_A and θ_B are independent. We note that this is the case and that Eqs. (2-40) and (2-44) are valid even when $\overline{A(t)} \neq 0$ and $\overline{B(t)} \neq 0$, if we subtract from the process its mean, and if T is sufficiently large. This fact will not be proved here, since it is not needed for the subsequent analysis.

We have called the random variable θ normal if the probability that it lies in the interval $(x, x + \delta)$ is given by (2-34). It follows from this definition that the probability that $\theta > x$ is given by

$$P(\theta > x) = \frac{1}{\sqrt{2\pi}} \int_x^{\infty} e^{-z^2/2}\, dz = \frac{1}{\sqrt{2\pi}} \int_{-\infty}^{-x} e^{-z^2/2}\, dz = V(x) \tag{2-47}$$

The value of this integral can be found in tables. We have introduced the function $V(x)$ because it will be very often encountered below. It is shown graphically in Figure 2-1. The probability that $\theta < x$ is

$$P(\theta < x) = 1 - V(x) = V(-x) \tag{2-48}$$

The mean value of θ is

$$E\theta = 0 \tag{2-49}$$

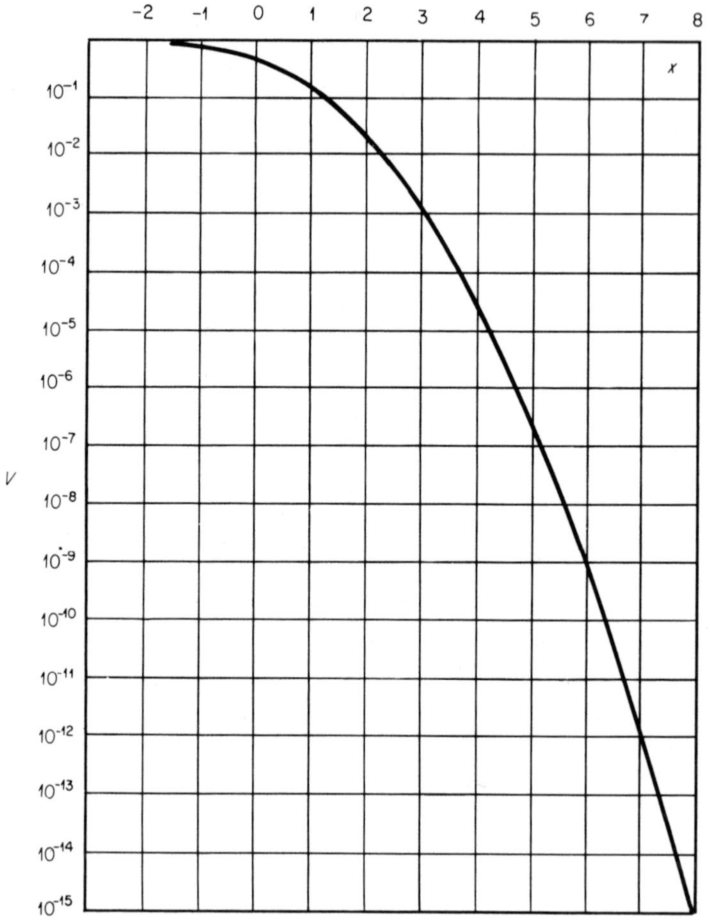

$$V(x) = \frac{1}{\sqrt{2\pi}} \int_{-\infty}^{-x} e^{\frac{-z^2}{2}} dz$$

Fig. 2-1.

The mean value of θ^2 is

$$D\theta = E\theta^2 = 1 \qquad (2\text{-}50)$$

2-4 Representation of normal fluctuation noise as a Fourier series

The normal fluctuation noise introduced in Section 2-3 can be represented as the Fourier series

$$W(t) = \sum_{\ell=1}^{\infty} w_\ell I_\ell(t) \qquad (2\text{-}51)$$

(if we neglect the constant component), where

$$w_\ell = \overline{W(t) I_\ell(t)} \qquad (2\text{-}52)$$

If $\ell > 0$, but is not so large that the period of the harmonic is of the same order of magnitude as the length of the noise pulses, then according to (2-40)

$$w_\ell = \frac{\sigma}{\sqrt{2T}} \theta_\ell \qquad (2\text{-}53)$$

Thus, if we pick out from the noise the components with frequencies from $f_\mu = \mu/T$ to $f_\nu = \nu/T$, where $\mu \geq 1$, and ν is not too large, then these components are

$$\begin{aligned} W_{\mu,\nu}(t) &= \sum_{\ell=\ell_1}^{\ell_2} \frac{\sigma}{\sqrt{2T}} I_\ell(t)\,\theta_\ell = \frac{\sigma}{\sqrt{2T}} \sum_{\ell=2\mu-1}^{\ell_2} I_\ell(t)\,\theta_\ell \\ &= \frac{\sigma}{\sqrt{T}} \sum_{\ell=\mu}^{\nu} (\theta_{2\ell-1} \sin \ell \frac{2\pi}{T} t + \theta_{2\ell} \cos \ell \frac{2\pi}{T} t) \end{aligned} \qquad (2\text{-}54)$$

where $\ell_1 = 2\mu-1$, $\ell_2 = 2\nu$. The quantities θ_ℓ figuring in this expression are constant on the interval $-T/2, +T/2$, but, as random variables, they can be different for different noise samples. It should also be noted that, according to Section 2-3, all the θ_ℓ are (mutually) independent, since all the $I_\ell(t)$ are (mutually) orthogonal.

The process $W_{\mu,\nu}(t)$ will be called normal fluctuation noise with constant intensity in the frequency range μ/T to ν/T. The mean square of this process over time T is, according to (2-23) and (2-54)

$$\overline{W^2_{\mu,\nu}(t)} = \frac{\sigma^2}{2T} \sum_{\ell=2\mu-1}^{\ell_2} \theta_\ell^2 \qquad (2\text{-}55)$$

Averaging with respect to realizations of the process, we obtain for the square of the effective value the expression

$$H^2 = E\,\overline{W^2_{\mu,\nu}(t)} = \frac{\sigma^2}{2T} \sum_{\ell=2\mu-1}^{\ell_2} E\,\theta^2_\ell \tag{2-56}$$

and, since $E\theta^2_\ell = 1$, we have

$$H^2 = E\,\overline{W^2_{\mu,\nu}(t)} = \frac{\sigma^2}{2T}(2\nu - 2\mu) = \sigma^2(f_\nu - f_\mu) \tag{2-57}$$

whence

$$\sigma = \sqrt{\frac{E\,\overline{W^2_{\mu,\nu}(t)}}{f_\nu - f_\mu}} = \frac{H}{\sqrt{f_\nu - f_\mu}} \tag{2-58}$$

Thus, σ is the effective value of the process $W_{\mu,\nu}(t)$, referred to unit bandwidth.

We now show that if the waveforms $A(t)$ and $B(t)$ satisfy the condition

$$\overline{A(t)} = 0, \qquad \overline{B(t)} = 0, \qquad \overline{A(t)\,B(t)} = 0 \tag{2-59}$$

and can be represented as Fourier series which have no components with frequencies less than $f_\mu = \mu/T$ and greater than $f_\nu = \nu/T$, then

$$\overline{W_{\mu,\nu}(t)\,A(t)} = \frac{\sigma}{\sqrt{2T}}\sqrt{\overline{A^2(t)}}\;\theta_A \tag{2-60}$$

$$W_{\mu,\nu}(t)\,B(t) = \frac{\sigma}{\sqrt{2T}}\sqrt{\overline{B^2(t)}}\;\theta_B \tag{2-61}$$

where θ_A and θ_B are independent normal random variables. Indeed, the process (2-51) can be written as

$$W(t) = W'(t) + W_{\mu,\nu}(t) + W''(t) \tag{2-62}$$

where

$$W'(t) = \sum_{\ell=1}^{2\mu-2} w_\ell I_\ell(t) \tag{2-63}$$

$$W''(t) = \sum_{\ell=2\nu+1}^{\infty} w_\ell I_\ell(t) \tag{2-64}$$

Then, by hypothesis, $W'(t)$ and $W''(t)$ have no components with frequencies coinciding with the frequencies of the components of the oscillations $A(t)$ and $B(t)$. Therefore

$$\overline{W'(t)\,A(t)} = 0, \qquad \overline{W''(t)\,A(t)} = 0,$$
$$\overline{W'(t)\,B(t)} = 0, \qquad \overline{W''(t)\,B(t)} = 0 \tag{2-65}$$

whence, multiplying both sides of (2-62) by A(t) and B(t) and taking the scalar product, we obtain the expressions (2-60) and (2-61), with the help of Eqs. (2-40) and (2-44).

For simplicity, we shall often consider the random function

$$\text{Ⓗ}(t) = \sum_{\ell=2\mu-1}^{\ell_2} \theta_\ell I_\ell(t) = \sum_{\ell=1}^{n} \theta'_\ell I'_\ell(t) \tag{2-66}$$

which differs from the process $W_{\mu,\nu}(t)$ by the constant factor $\frac{\sigma}{\sqrt{2T}}$. Here we have written

$$\theta'_\ell = \theta_{\ell+2\mu-2}, \quad I'_\ell(t) = I_{\ell+2\mu-2}(t), \quad n = 2\nu - (2\mu - 2) \tag{2-67}$$

According to (2-60), we have

$$\text{Ⓗ}(t)\,A(t) = \sqrt{\overline{A^2(t)}}\;\theta_A \tag{2-68}$$

since $W_{\mu,\nu}(t)$ equals Ⓗ(t) if $\frac{\sigma}{\sqrt{2T}} = 1$.

2-5 Linear functions of independent normal random variables

We shall now find the linear function

$$\sum_{\ell=1}^{n} a_\ell \theta_\ell \tag{2-69}$$

of the independent normal random variables θ_ℓ, where the a_ℓ are arbitrary constants. We set

$$A(t) = \sum_{\ell=1}^{n} a_\ell I_\ell(t) \tag{2-70}$$

$$\text{Ⓗ}(t) = \sum_{\ell=1}^{n} \theta_\ell I_\ell(t) \tag{2-71}$$

Then, according to (2-22)

$$\overline{A(t)\,\text{Ⓗ}(t)} = \sum_{\ell=1}^{n} a_\ell \theta_\ell \tag{2-72}$$

On the other hand, by (2-68) and (2-23)

$$\overline{A(t)\Theta(t)} = \sqrt{\overline{A^2(t)}}\;\theta_A = \sqrt{\sum_{\ell=1}^{n} a_\ell^2}\;\theta_A \tag{2-73}$$

whence

$$\sum_{\ell=1}^{n} a_\ell \theta_\ell = \sqrt{\sum_{\ell=1}^{n} a_\ell^2}\;\theta_A \tag{2-74}$$

Analogously, we have

$$\sum_{\ell=1}^{n} b_\ell \theta_\ell = \sqrt{\sum_{\ell=1}^{n} b_\ell^2}\;\theta_B \tag{2-75}$$

Moreover, if

$$\sum_{\ell=1}^{n} a_\ell b_\ell = 0 \tag{2-76}$$

then θ_A and θ_B are independent normal random variables; for, writing

$$B(t) = \sum_{\ell=1}^{n} b_\ell I_\ell(t) \tag{2-77}$$

we find (as above)

$$\overline{B(t)\Theta(t)} = \sum_{\ell=1}^{n} b_\ell \theta_\ell = \sqrt{\sum_{\ell=1}^{n} b_\ell^2}\;\theta_B$$

where, according to (2-76) and (2-22), $\overline{A(t)\,B(t)} = 0$, and therefore, by (2-60) and (2-61) θ_A and θ_B are independent.

2-6 The probability that normal fluctuation noise falls in a given region

We shall say that a function lies in a given region if its coordinates satisfy the conditions that define the region. We now find the probability that the function (2-66) lies in the elementary region defined by the conditions

$$\begin{aligned} y_1 &< \theta'_1 < y_1 + dy_1 \\ &\cdots\cdots\cdots\cdots \\ y_n &< \theta'_n < y_n + dy_n \end{aligned} \tag{2-78}$$

Since the θ'_ℓ figuring in these inequalities are independent random variables which satisfy the conditions (2-34), the probability that all the inequalities (2-78) are simultaneously satisified is

$$P(2\text{-}78) = \frac{dy_1}{\sqrt{2\pi}} \exp(-y_1^2/2) \frac{dy_2}{\sqrt{2\pi}} \exp(-y_2^2/2) \cdots \frac{dy_n}{\sqrt{2\pi}} \exp(-y_n^2/2)$$

$$= \frac{dy_1\, dy_2 \cdots dy_n}{(2\pi)^{n/2}} \exp(-\frac{1}{2} \sum_{\ell=1}^{n} y_\ell^2) \tag{2-79}$$

The probability that the function $\Theta(t)$ will lie in some region, say the region R, which can be divided up into elementary regions of the type (2-78), is obviously equal to the sum of the probabilities that the function will fall in one of the elementary regions into which the region R is subdivided. Since the elementary regions are infinitely small, this sum reduces to the integral

$$P(\Theta(t) \text{ in } R) = \iint_R \cdots \int \frac{dy_1\, dy_2 \cdots dy_n}{(2\pi)^{n/2}} \exp(-\frac{1}{2} \sum_{i=1}^{n} y_i^2) \tag{2-80}$$

which is to be taken over the values $y_1, \ldots, y_n$ belonging to R.

In the case where the region R is so small that $\sum_{i=1}^{n} y_i^2$ can be regarded as constant in integrating over the region, then the exponential can be taken out from behind the integral sign, and we obtain

$$P(\Theta(t) \text{ in } R) = (2\pi)^{-n/2} \exp(-\frac{1}{2} \sum_{i=1}^{n} y_i^2)\, \Delta V \tag{2-81}$$

where

$$\Delta V = \iint_R \cdots \int dy_1\, dy_2 \cdots dy_n \tag{2-82}$$

Using the terminology of three-dimensional space, we shall call the quantity ΔV the <u>volume of the region R.</u>

If a function

$$Y(t) = \sum_{i=1}^{n} y_i\, I_i'(t) \tag{2-83}$$

lies in the region R, then the coordinates of the function can be put into the formula (2-81). According to Eq. (2-23), we have

$$\overline{Y^2(t)} = \sum_{i=1}^{n} y_i^2 \tag{2-84}$$

so that

$$P(\Theta(t) \text{ in } R) = \frac{\Delta V}{(2\pi)^{n/2}} \exp(-\frac{1}{2}\, \overline{Y^2(t)}) \tag{2-85}$$

We can draw the following conclusion from this formula. The probability that the random function $\Theta(t)$ defined by Eq. (2-66) lies in a small region in which the function $Y(t)$ also lies, is proportional to the volume of the region, and depends in addition only on the effective value of the function $Y(t)$, decreasing as the effective value increases. By a small region we mean here a region such that the effective value of all functions lying in it can be regarded as the same in calculating the integral (2-80).

2-7 Geometric interpretation of our results

The results obtained in this chapter, as well as the results which we shall obtain below, can be interpreted by using the geometry of n-dimensional space. Although it is not very easy to visualize n-dimensional space, still such an interpretation has many advantages, especially for those who are inclined to think in geometric terms. The point is that relations which are valid for any n-dimensional space are valid in particular for the special cases of two and three-dimensional space. This allows one to guess and verify general properties of spaces with many dimensions with the aid of the descriptive models of ordinary geometry. Moreover, the use of terminology and models borrowed from the geometry of three-dimensional space allows one to more easily keep in mind the results which have been obtained.

We were agreed to deal with functions in an interval T and with frequencies lying in certain bands. In this case, the functions being considered can be represented in the form

$$A(t) = \sum_{\ell=2\mu-1}^{2\nu} a_\ell I_\ell(t)$$

where the $I_\ell(t)$ are specified functions given by Eq. (2-14). Thus, any function under consideration is completely determined by $n = 2\nu - 2\mu$ quantities a_ℓ. We can represent this function conventionally either by a radius vector in n-dimensional space, the terminal point of which has coordinates $a_{2\mu-1}, a_{2\mu}, \ldots, a_{2\nu}$, or by the terminal point itself. Such a vector will be called the vector corresponding to the function $A(t)$ or briefly the <u>vector</u> of the function $A(t)$. In the case $n = 2$, this representation is especially graphic.

The function $I_\ell(t)$ has all coordinates equal to zero except the coordinate with index ℓ, which equals one. Thus, the radius vector corresponding to $I_\ell(t)$ lies on the axis indexed by ℓ, and has unit length.

It is not hard to see that the vector of a sum of functions equals the sum of the vectors of the individual functions. The vector of the difference of two functions is the difference of the vectors of the individual functions. According to the definitions of Section 2-1, the scalar product of two functions equals the scalar product of the vectors corresponding to them, as follows from Eq. (2-22). Thus, addition, subtraction, and scalar multiplication of functions can be replaced by addition, subtraction, and multiplication of their vectors.

Furthermore, orthogonal functions correspond to orthogonal vectors, and functions which coincide in direction correspond to vectors which coincide in direction.

The magnitude of the effective value of a function, the square of which is given by the expression (2-23), equals the length of the vector corresponding to the function. Accordingly, the square of the distance between the points which correspond to the functions $A(t)$ and $B(t)$ equals $\overline{(A(t) - B(t))^2}$. A unit vector corresponds to a normalized function. A system of orthonormal vectors corresponds to a system of orthonormal functions. The notion of the volume of a region, introduced in Eq. (2-82) of Section 2-6, corresponds to volume in the space in which we construct the vectors.

To the random function $\textcircled{H}(t)$ defined by Eq. (2-66) there corresponds a random radius vector. The probability that the end of this vector falls in some small volume ΔV is given by Eq. (2-85). As is evident from the formula, this probability is proportional to the volume ΔV, and depends also on the distance of the volume from the origin of coordinates. This distance is equal to the quantity $\sqrt{\overline{Y^2(t)}}$. It follows from Eq. (2-68) that the projection on any direction of the vector corresponding to $\textcircled{H}(t)$ is equal to the scalar product of the unit vector coinciding with the given direction and the vector corresponding to $\textcircled{H}(t)$, and is always a normal random variable. The projections of the vector corresponding to $\textcircled{H}(t)$ on orthogonal directions are mutually independent normal random variables. Everything which has been said here about the vector corresponding to the random waveform $\textcircled{H}(t)$ can be carried over to the vector corresponding to the noise waveform $W_{\mu,\nu}(t)$, since these waveforms differ only by a constant factor.

PART II
TRANSMISSION OF DISCRETE MESSAGES

CHAPTER 3
THE IDEAL RECEIVER FOR DISCRETE SIGNALS

3-1 Discrete messages and signals

In this part we shall consider the transmission of discrete messages, i.e., of messages which can have a finite number of completely specified versions; we shall also consider the effect of noise on the transmission of such messages. As already mentioned, the category of transmission of discrete messages includes telegraphy, remote-control when there is provision for a finite number of distinct commands, various kinds of signalling, etc. We shall use the example of telegraphy to make more precise what we mean by a message. As already noted, in general by a message we mean that which is to be transmitted. Thus, we shall designate as a message an entire telegram, the separate words of which it consists, and the separate symbols of which the words consist. It is also possible to call a message the voltage waveform which corresponds to the transmitted word or symbol, and which is produced by the telegraph transmitter, to be transmitted to the telegraph receiver. This voltage waveform usually consists of individual smaller units, which follow one another in sequence. For example, when the five-symbol telegraph code is used, the voltage waveform corresponding to one symbol consists of five units. We can also regard each of these units as a message. Thus, we can mean by a message both the text of the telegram and the elements which go to make it up, as well as the voltage waveforms produced by the telegraph transmitter and their elements. A message can be complex and can consist of a series of simpler messages which follow one another in sequence. For simplicity, we shall assume that in the case where the telegraph transmitter sends nothing, a message is sent to the effect that the telegraph receiver should print nothing. The receiver has to reproduce the transmitted message. Therefore, in the case where we take as the message the separate symbols, words, or telegrams, the telegraph printer must be included as a component of the receiver.

Suppose the system in question provides for the transmission of messages which can take on m values. We assume that to each value of the message corresponds a definite signal (i.e., waveform) which acts upon the receiver when the message is transmitted in the absence of noise. We designate those m values of the signal by

$$A_1(t),\ A_2(t),\ \ldots\ ,\ A_m(t) \tag{3-1}$$

In particular, one of these signals can be zero. Using Eq. (2-21), we can represent these signals as

$$A_k(t) = \sum_{\ell=\ell_1}^{\ell_2} a_{k\ell} I_\ell(t) \tag{3-2}$$

Suppose noise is added to these signal waveforms. We assume that for all frequencies involved in the sum the intensity of the noise is the same and equals σ. In this case, when the signal A(t) is transmitted, the sum voltage acting on the receiver is

$$X(t) = \sum_{\ell=\ell_1}^{\ell_2} x_\ell I_\ell(t) = W_{\mu,\nu}(t) + A_k(t) \tag{3-3}$$

where $W_{\mu,\nu}(t)$ is the noise waveform defined by Eq. (2-54). In this expression, we sum over all frequencies to which the receiver can respond. Using Eqs. (3-2), (3-3) and (2-54), we obtain

$$x_\ell = \frac{\sigma}{\sqrt{2T}} \theta_\ell + a_{k\ell} \tag{3-4}$$

The waveform X(t) acting on the receiver is completely characterized by the coordinates $x_{\ell_1}, x_{\ell_1+1}, \ldots, x_{\ell_2}$.

3-2 The ideal receiver

We shall assume that, depending on the waveform which acts upon it, the receiver always reproduces one of the possible messages. It is clear that for every receiver we can pick out from all possible values of X(t) (i. e., all possible values of the set $x_{\ell_1}, x_{\ell_1+1}, \ldots, x_{\ell_2}$) the domain of values for which the receiver will reproduce the message corresponding to the signal $A_1(t)$. We shall call this domain <u>the domain of the signal</u> $A_1(t)$. Then, in just the same way, we can pick out the domain of values for which the message corresponding to the signal $A_2(t)$ will be reproduced. We call this domain <u>the domain of the signal</u> $A_2(t)$, and so forth. It is clear that in this fashion the whole domain of possible values of X(t) will be divided into m non-overlapping subdomains.

Suppose the signal $A_k(t)$ was sent. In this case, the waveform X(t) which arrives at the receiver in the presence of noise is characterized by the coordinates (3-4), which in general can take on arbitrary values, since the θ_ℓ are (mutually) independent normal random variables. Then there is a finite probability that the waveform X(t) will fall in any domain. Assume that it falls in the domain $A_i(t)$, where $i \neq k$. Then the receiver will incorrectly reproduce the message corresponding to the signal $A_i(t)$ instead of the message corresponding to the signal $A_k(t)$. It is clear that the number of correctly reproduced messages depends on the configuration of the domains defined by the receiver.

We shall be concerned with the problem of selecting the domains of values of the waveforms $X(t)$, for given signals (3-1), in such a way as to make the number of incorrectly reproduced messages as small as possible, or, what amounts to the same thing, in such a way as to make the probability of correctly reproduced messages as large as possible. The receiver which is characterized by such domains, and which therefore gives the minimum number of incorrectly received messages, will be called ideal. To determine the configuration of the domains which characterize the ideal receiver, we introduce the following notation:

$P(A_k)$ is the a priori probability that the signal A_k is sent.

$P_{A_k}(X)$ is the conditional probability that the waveform $X(t)$ with coordinates

$$y_{\ell_1} < x_{\ell_1} < y_{\ell_1} + dy_{\ell_1}, \ \ldots \ , y_{\ell_2} < x_{\ell_2} < y_{\ell_2} + dy_{\ell_2} \tag{3-5}$$

will be received, if it is known that the signal $A_k(t)$ was sent.

$P_X(A_k)$ is the conditional probability that the signal $A_k(t)$ was sent, if we know that the received waveform is $X(t)$, i.e., that it corresponds to the inequalities (3-5).

$P(X) = \sum_{k=1}^{n} P(A_k) P_{A_k}(X)$ is the probability that the received signal is $X(t)$.

With this notation, the joint probability that the signal $A_k(t)$ is sent and that the waveform $X(t)$ is received is given by

$$P(A_k) P_{A_k}(X) = P(X) P_X(A_k) \tag{3-6}$$

whence

$$P_X(A_k) = \frac{P(A_k) P_{A_k}(X)}{P(X)} = \frac{P(A_k) P_{A_k}(X)}{\sum_{\ell=1}^{m} P(A_\ell) P_{A_\ell}(X)} \tag{3-7}$$

If, when the waveform $X(t)$ is received, the receiver reproduces the message corresponding to the signal $A_k(t)$, then the probability of there being correct reproduction when $X(t)$ is received is obviously $P_X(A_k)$. Similarly, if, when the waveform $X(t)$ is received, the receiver reproduces the message corresponding to the waveform $A_\ell(t)$, then the probability of correct reproduction is $P_X(A_\ell)$. Thus, to obtain the maximum probability of correct signal reproduction, when $X(t)$ is received, the receiver should reproduce the message which corresponds to the signal for which the quantity $P_X(A_k)$ is largest; in other words, the receiver should be constructed in such a way as to make $X(t)$ belong to the domain of the signal $A_k(t)$ for which $P_X(A_k)$ is the largest. This receiver will guarantee the maximum probability of correct message reproduction. No other receiver can increase this probability.

According to (3-7), when the waveform X(t) is received, the ideal receiver should reproduce the message corresponding to the signal which gives the largest value of the expression

$$P(A_k)\, P_{A_k}(X) \tag{3-8}$$

The quantity $P(A_k)$ in this expression has to be furnished; it is determined by the character of the transmitted messages. The quantity $P_{A_k}(X)$ is by definition the probability that the noise assumes a value which when added to the signal $A_k(t)$ gives the waveform X(t) satisfying the relations (3-5). It follows from Eq. (3-4) that this probability is the probability that the θ_ℓ satisfy the inequalities

$$\frac{\sqrt{2T}}{\sigma}(y_{\ell_1} - a_{\ell_1 k}) < \theta_{\ell_1} < \frac{\sqrt{2T}}{\sigma}(y_{\ell_1} - a_{\ell_1 k} + dy_{\ell_1})$$

$$\cdots\cdots\cdots\cdots \tag{3-9}$$

$$\frac{\sqrt{2T}}{\sigma}(y_{\ell_2} - a_{\ell_2 k}) < \theta_{\ell_2} < \frac{\sqrt{2T}}{\sigma}(y_{\ell_2} - a_{\ell_2 k} + dy_{\ell_2})$$

According to Section 2-6 and Eqs. (2-78) and (2-79), the latter probability is

$$P_{A_k}(X) = \left(\frac{2T}{\sigma^2}\right)^{n/2} \frac{dy_{\ell_1} \cdots dy_{\ell_2}}{(2\pi)^{n/2}} \exp\left[-\frac{T}{\sigma^2}\sum_{\ell=\ell_1}^{\ell_2}(y_\ell - a_{k\ell})^2\right]$$

where $n = \ell_2 - \ell_1 + 1$. Moreover, for infinitesimally small $dy_{\ell_1}, \ldots, dy_{\ell_2}$, we have

$$\sum_{\ell=\ell_1}^{\ell_2}(y_\ell - a_{k\ell})^2 = \sum_{\ell=\ell_1}^{\ell_2}(x_\ell - a_{k\ell})^2 = \overline{(X(t) - A_k(t))^2}$$

whence it follows that

$$P(A_k)\, P_{A_k}(X) = \frac{dy_{\ell_1} \cdots dy_{\ell_2}}{(\pi/T)^{n/2}\,\sigma^2} \exp - \left[\frac{T}{\sigma^2}\overline{(X(t) - A_k(t))^2} - \ln P(A_k)\right] \tag{3-10}$$

where the larger the value of the exponent, the smaller the value of (3-10). <u>Thus we obtain the largest probability of correct message reproduction if we choose the receiver in such a way as to make</u> X(t) <u>belong to the domain of the signal for which the quantity</u>

$$T\,\overline{(X(t) - A_k(t))^2} - \sigma^2 \ln P(A_k) = \int_{-T/2}^{+T/2}(X(t) - A_k(t))^2\, dt - \sigma^2 \ln P(A_k) \tag{3-11}$$

<u>has the smallest value.</u>

3-3 Geometric interpretation of the material of chapter 3

As we have already remarked, every waveform of finite length and with a finite frequency spectrum can be represented as a point or radius vector in n-space. Thus, each of the m signals considered in this chapter can be represented by its own point or radius vector. If to the transmitted signal is added a noise waveform with a vector which can have an arbitrary direction and arbitrary length, then the resulting received waveform $X(t)$ will also be characterized by a point in n-space, which most often will not coincide with any of the points corresponding to signals. Depending on the position of this point, the receiver will reproduce some message or other. If we combine all the points of our space which correspond to received waveforms for which the receiver reproduces the message corresponding to the signal $A_k(t)$, we obtain the region of space which we called the domain of the signal $A_k(t)$. Since we assumed that when a waveform is received, one of the possible messages has to be reproduced, then every point of space has to fall in the domain of some signal. We saw how these domains should be chosen for the ideal receiver. In the simplest case, when all the signals are equiprobable (i. e., when all the $P(A_k)$ are equal), the domain of the signal $A_k(t)$ should consist of points of the space which lie closer to the point $A_k(t)$ than to any other point representing a signal, i. e., points for which

$$\overline{(X(t) - A_k(t))^2} < \overline{(X(t) - A_\ell(t))^2}$$

where $A_\ell(t)$ is any of the possible signals which differs from $A_k(t)$. This is natural, since the smaller the length of the noise vector, the larger the probability of the noise, and therefore it is most likely that the given received waveform was formed by the addition of the noise vector to the end of the <u>nearest</u> signal vector.

CHAPTER 4

NOISE IMMUNITY FOR SIGNALS WITH TWO DISCRETE VALUES

4-1 Probability of error for the ideal receiver

Even with the ideal receiver there sometimes occurs incorrect message reproduction, because of the perturbation of the signal waveform by the added noise. We now find the probability of such incorrect reproduction, or, as we say, the probability of error. This probability characterizes the noise immunity for reception with the ideal receiver, i. e., the optimum noise immunity for the given kind of signals. The probability of error for reception with a real receiver can attain this value, but cannot be less than it.

In this chapter we consider noise immunity for signals which can take on only two values $A_1(t)$ and $A_2(t)$. This case is of great practical interest, since discrete signals often consist of sequences of elementary signals, each of which can have only two values. According to what was said in Section 3-2, the ideal receiver in this case should reproduce the message corresponding to the signal $A_1(t)$ if

$$T\ \overline{(X(t) - A_1(t))^2} - \sigma^2 \ln P(A_1) < T\ \overline{(X(t) - A_2(t))^2} - \sigma^2 \ln P(A_2) \qquad (4\text{-}1)$$

and otherwise the message corresponding to the signal $A_2(t)$.

Suppose the signal $A_1(t)$ was sent. We now find the probability that the noise (of constant intensity in the frequency range μ/T to ν/T) assumes a value such that the ideal receiver reproduces the message corresponding to the signal $A_2(t)$. This probability equals the probability that the inequality (4-1) is not satisfied when we substitute into it the quantity

$$X(t) = A_1(t) + W_{\mu,\nu}(t)$$

i. e., the probability that the inequality

$$T\ \overline{W^2_{\mu,\nu}(t)} - \sigma^2 \ln P(A_1) > T\ \overline{(W_{\mu,\nu}(t) + A_1(t) - A_2(t))^2} - \sigma^2 \ln P(A_2)$$

is satisfied. Expanding this expression according to the rules introduced in Section 2-1, we obtain

$$T\ \overline{W^2_{\mu,\nu}(t)} - \sigma^2 \ln P(A_1) > T\ \overline{W^2_{\mu,\nu}(t)} + 2T\ \overline{W_{\mu,\nu}(t)\,(A_1(t) - A_2(t))}$$
$$+ T\ \overline{(A_1(t) - A_2(t))^2} - \sigma^2 \ln P(A_2)$$

whence it follows by Eq. (2-60) that

$$-\sigma^2 \ln P(A_1) > \sigma\sqrt{2T}\sqrt{\overline{(A_1(t) - A_2(t))^2}}\;\theta + T\;\overline{(A_1(t) - A_2(t))^2} - \sigma^2 \ln P(A_2)$$

or

$$\theta < \frac{1}{2}\ln\frac{P(A_2)}{P(A_1)}\;\frac{\sqrt{2}\,\sigma}{\sqrt{T\,\overline{(A_1(t) - A_2(t))^2}}} - \frac{\sqrt{T\,\overline{(A_1(t) - A_2(t))^2}}}{\sqrt{2}\,\sigma}$$

The probability of this inequality can be determined from Eq. (2-48). Thus, the probability that as a result of the addition of fluctuation noise to the signal $A_1(t)$, the ideal receiver reproduces the incorrect message corresponding to the signal $A_2(t)$, equals

$$P(A_2 \text{ instead of } A_1) = V(\alpha_{21}) \tag{4-2}$$

where we have introduced the notation

$$\alpha_{21} = \alpha + \frac{1}{2\alpha}\ln\frac{P(A_1)}{P(A_2)} \tag{4-3}$$

$$\alpha = \frac{\sqrt{T\,\overline{(A_1(t) - A_2(t))^2}}}{\sqrt{2}\,\sigma} = \left[\frac{1}{2\sigma^2}\int_{-T/2}^{+T/2}(A_1(t) - A_2(t))^2\,dt\right]^{1/2} \tag{4-4}$$

and V is given by Figure 2-1.

In just the same way, the probability that the receiver will incorrectly interpret the transmitted signal $A_2(t)$ as $A_1(t)$ is found to be

$$P(A_1 \text{ instead of } A_2) = V(\alpha_{12}) \tag{4-5}$$

where

$$\alpha_{12} = \alpha + \frac{1}{2\alpha}\ln\frac{P(A_2)}{P(A_2)} \tag{4-6}$$

It follows that in the case of two signals the probability of error for the ideal receiver is

$$P_E = P(A_1)\,V(\alpha_{21}) + P(A_2)\,V(\alpha_{12}) \tag{4-7}$$

As is apparent from these formulas, the probability of error, which determines the optimum noise immunity, depends on two factors--on the ratio $P(A_1)/P(A_2)$, and on

$$\alpha^2 = \frac{T\ \overline{(A_1(t) - A_2(t))^2}}{2\sigma^2} = \frac{1}{2\sigma^2} \int_{-T/2}^{+T/2} (A_1(t) - A_2(t))^2\, dt$$

The first factor depends exclusively on the transmitted messages. The second factor depends on the ratio of the specific energy of the signal difference to σ^2, the square of the noise intensity. The larger this ratio, the smaller the probability of error, and the larger the optimum noise immunity. In this factor, for a given noise intensity, we can change only the specific energy of the signal difference. Systems for which this energy is the largest afford the best noise immunity, provided that the receivers are sufficiently good.

In geometric terms, both α and the optimum noise immunity are determined by the distance $\sqrt{\overline{(A_1(t) - A_2(t))^2}}$ between the points representing the signal, and become larger when this distance increases. We note also that the probability of error does not depend on the expansion interval T, since by hypothesis this expansion interval can be taken large enough to have the signal entirely contained within the interval $(-T/2, +T/2)$. It also does not depend on the limits of the frequency summation, provided they include all frequencies contained in the signals. The probability of error is connected with the mean number of incorrectly received messages by the following relation: the number of incorrectly received messages is on the average equal to NP_E, where N is the number of transmitted signals.

4-2 Influence of the ratio $P(A_1)/P(A_2)$

If the probability of transmission is the same for both signals (i.e., $P(A_1) = P(A_2) = \frac{1}{a}$), Eq. (4-7) simplifies to

$$P_E = V(\alpha) \tag{4-8}$$

In the case where the noise intensity σ is small, so that $\alpha \gg 1$, the second term in the expressions for α_{21} and α_{12} can be neglected, and since $P(A_1) + P(A_2) = 1$, in this case also Eq. (4-7) reduces to Eq. (4-8). In Figure 4-1, curve 1 gives the dependence of P_E on α for the case $P(A_1)/P(A_2) = 1$, and curve 2 gives the same dependence for the case $P(A_1)/P(A_2) = 10$ or 0.1. These curves were obtained from Eqs. (4-8) and (4-7), respectively. As is evident from these curves, and also from an analysis of the formulas, P_E gets smaller as $P(A_1)/P(A_2)$ differs more from unity. In the limit $P(A_1)/P(A_2) = \infty$ or 0, we obtain $P_E = 0$, irrespective of α. This result is obvious, since in this case the transmitted signal is known in advance.

In the case $P(A_1) = P(A_2)$, the domains which the ideal receiver assigns to the signals $A_1(t)$ and $A_2(t)$ do not depend on the noise intensity σ, as follows from Eq. (4-1). In the case $P(A_1) \neq P(A_2)$, they must depend on σ. This means that the regime of the ideal receiver has to change with σ, which in many cases may be inconvenient. Let us see how much the probability of incorrect signal reproduction increases if the signal domains (i.e., the receiver regime) are taken for the case where $P(A_1) = P(A_2)$, or, what amounts to the same thing, for the case of small σ, and are not changed in the case where $P(A_1) \neq P(A_2)$ and σ is large. For the case where σ is small, according to (3-11), the receiver domains are chosen so that the received waveform $X(t)$ falls in the domain of the signal $A_1(t)$ if

$$\overline{(X(t) - A_1(t))^2} < \overline{(X(t) - A_2(t))^2}$$

If we repeat the considerations of Section 4-1 for this case, we obtain

$$P(A_2 \text{ instead of } A_1) = V(\alpha)$$

where α is defined by Eq. (4-4). In complete analogy, we have

$$P(A_1 \text{ instead of } A_2) = V(\alpha)$$

whence the probability of error in this case equals

$$\begin{aligned} P_E &= P(A_1)\, P(A_2 \text{ instead of } A_1) + P(A_2)\, P(A_1 \text{ instead of } A_2) \\ &= V(\alpha) \end{aligned} \qquad (4\text{-}9)$$

since $P(A_1) + P(A_2) = 1$. Thus, this probability does not depend on the ratio $P(A_1)/P(A_2)$, and equals the probability of error for reception with the ideal receiver in the case $P(A_1)/P(A_2) = 1$.

Now consider the case $P(A_1)/P(A_2) = 10$ or 0.1. Then, the probability of error for reception with an ideal receiver, specially constructed for this case, is given by curve 2 of Figure 4-1. On the other hand, the probability of error for reception with the receiver just considered is given by curve 1 of the same figure. As is evident from the figure, for small α the difference between the two curves can be quite substantial, and in this case it is desirable to take into account the unequal probabilities of signal transmission. For operation in the region of small σ (i.e., large α) the difference is small.

To characterize how much a given receiver approaches the ideal receiver in noise immunity, we introduce the concept of the <u>efficiency coefficient</u> of a receiver, which we designate by η. By this coefficient we mean the ratio of the signal power for the ideal receiver to the signal power for some other receiver under consideration, provided that the probability of error and the form of the signals are the same in both cases. Thus,

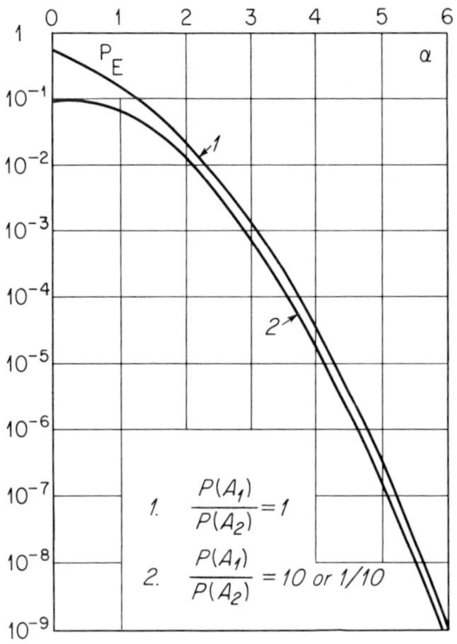

Fig. 4-1. Probability of error for the ideal receiver. Curve 1 is for $P(A_1)/P(A_2) = 1$; curve 2 is for $P(A_1)/P(A_2) = 10$ or 0.1; α is defined by Eq. (4-4).

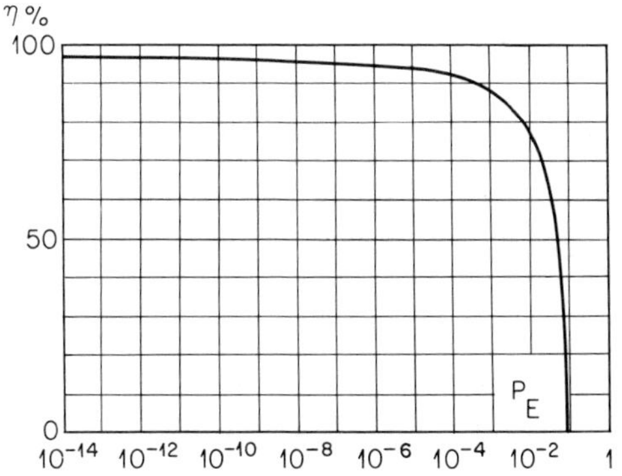

Fig. 4-2. Dependence of the efficiency coefficient on the probability of error for $P(A_1)/P(A_2) = 10$ or 0.1, and for the receiver which is ideal for $P(A_1)/P(A_2) = 1$.

this coefficient shows how much the energy of the signals can be decreased, if we use the ideal receiver instead of the given receiver, while keeping fixed the probability of correct message reproduction. For the case just considered, this coefficient is equal to the square of the ratio of the abcissas of the curves 1 and 2 for the same value of P_E. The dependence of η on P_E which is obtained in this way is shown in Figure 4-2. As we see from this figure, for conditions such that $P_E < 10^{-3}$, and such conditions are common, we can take $\eta > 0.9$.

4-3 Optimum noise immunity for transmission with a passive space

In the case where the signal waveform can have only two values $A_1(t)$ and $A_2(t)$, and one of them, say $A_2(t)$, is identically zero, the transmission is called transmission with a passive space. If neither of the signals is identically zero, we refer to transmission with an active space. For transmission with a passive space, the value of α, which is defined by Eq. (4-4) and characterizes the optimum noise immunity, is given by

$$\alpha = \sqrt{\frac{T\,\overline{A_1^2(t)}}{2\sigma^2}} = \sqrt{\frac{1}{2\sigma^2}\int_{-T/2}^{+T/2} A_1^2(t)\,dt} \qquad (4\text{-}10)$$

Denoting the specific energy of the signal by

$$Q_1^2 = T\,\overline{A_1^2(t)} = \int_{-T/2}^{+T/2} A_1^2(t)\,dt \qquad (4\text{-}11)$$

we have

$$\alpha = \frac{1}{\sqrt{2}}\,\frac{Q_1}{\sigma} \qquad (4\text{-}12)$$

Thus, in this case the optimum noise immunity depends only on the signal energy and is completely independent of its shape. The larger the signal energy, the larger the optimum noise immunity. However, it should not be inferred from this result alone that the use of new signal forms and the improvement of receivers cannot raise the noise immunity of systems with a passive space. In fact, the noise immunity of systems now in use may be much less than the optimum noise immunity obtained above. When this is the case, it is clear that both the improvement of receivers and the use of new signal forms, which facilitate this improvement, can increase the noise immunity, and in the most favorable cases, make it approach the optimum noise immunity. To clarify this matter, in the next two sections, we consider an example of a real system with a passive space, and we find out how close its noise immunity is to the optimum.

4-4 Optimum noise immunity for the classical telegraph signal

As an example of transmission with a passive space, we consider the case of the classical elementary telegraph signal, which we shall take to be

$$A_1(t) = U_o \cos \omega_o t\,, \qquad \text{for} \quad 0 \leq t \leq \tau_o$$
$$A_1(t) = 0\,, \qquad \text{for} \quad t < 0 \quad \text{or} \quad t > \tau_o \tag{4-13}$$

and

$$A_2(t) = 0 \tag{4-14}$$

To determine the optimum noise immunity in this case, we can take α from Eq. (4-14). According to Appendix A and Eqs. (4-11) and (4-12), the quantity Q_1 which appears in this expression is given by

$$Q_1^2 = \frac{1}{2} \int_0^{\tau_o} U_o^2 \, dt = \frac{1}{2} U_o^2 \tau_o \tag{4-15}$$

Therefore, for the kind of transmission under consideration, we have by (4-12)

$$\alpha = \frac{U_o \sqrt{\tau_o}}{2\sigma} \tag{4-16}$$

According to Section 4-1, we can use the quantity α to determine the probability of error which characterizes the optimum noise immunity for this case.

4-5 Noise immunity for the classical telegraph signal and reception with a synchronous detector

Suppose to receive the signals considered in the previous section, we use a real receiver, such that the signals first go through a filter with a pass band from $\frac{\omega_o - \Omega}{2\pi}$ to $\frac{\omega_o + \Omega}{2\pi}$, and then enter a synchronous detector. The waveform at the detector output then enters a device which reproduces the message corresponding to the first signal if the voltage on its terminals at the time $\tau_o/2$ exceeds a certain value, and otherwise reproduces the message corresponding to the second signal. Such a process occurs, for example, when the voltage is rectified and used to activate a telegraph apparatus which operates on time division.

Regarding the filter as ideal, we have

$$u_s = \frac{U_o}{\pi} \left[\mathrm{Si}\,\Omega t - \mathrm{Si}\,\Omega(t - \tau_o) \right] \cos \omega_o t \tag{4-17}$$

for the signal at the output, as can be obtained with the use of the Fourier integral, if retardation in the filter is neglected. In this formula, Si denotes the sine integral, given by

$$\mathrm{Si}\, x = \int_{o}^{x} \frac{\sin z}{z}\, dz \qquad (4\text{-}18)$$

Clearly, the noise voltage after the filter consists of components with frequencies from $\frac{\omega_o - \Omega}{2\pi}$ to $\frac{\omega_o + \Omega}{2\pi}$, and has constant intensity σ in this band. According to Eq. (B-6) of Appendix B, this process can be written as

$$W_{\mu,\nu}(t) = \sqrt{2}\, W''_{1,n}(t) \cos \omega_o t + \sqrt{2}\, W'_{1,n}(t) \sin \omega_o t$$

where $W'_{1,n}(t)$ and $W''_{1,n}(t)$ are independent normal fluctuation noises, the components of which have frequencies from 0 to $n/T = \Omega/2\pi$, and have constant intensity σ in this band. Thus, if the signal $A_1(t)$ is sent, the sum voltage after the filter is

$$u'_f = u_s + W_{\mu,\nu}(t) = \left\{ \frac{U_o}{\pi} \left[\mathrm{Si}\,\Omega t - \mathrm{Si}\,\Omega(t - \tau_o)\right] + \sqrt{2}\, W''_{1,n}(t) \right\} \cos \omega_o t$$
$$+ \sqrt{2}\, W'_{1,n}(t) \sin \omega_o t \qquad (4\text{-}19)$$

The synchronous detector, as is well-known, gives at its output a voltage proportional to the amplitude of the component which coincides in phase with that of the received signal, and does not respond to the component which is 90° out of phase with the received signal. As stipulated, the output device reproduces the message corresponding to the signal $A_1(t)$ or $A_2(t)$, depending on the value of the voltage at the detector output at the time $t = \tau_o/2$. Designating this value by U_d, we obtain

$$U'_d = \frac{U_o}{\pi}\, 2\mathrm{Si}\, \frac{\Omega \tau_o}{2} + \sqrt{2}\, W''_{1,n}(\tau_o/2) \qquad (4\text{-}20)$$

If $A_1(t)$ is transmitted, and

$$U''_d = \sqrt{2}\, W''_{1,n}(\tau_o/2) \qquad (4\text{-}21)$$

if $A_2(t)$ is transmitted, i.e., if no signal at all is transmitted. The value of $W''_{1,n}(\tau_o/2)$ is a random variable; according to Eq. (C-2) of Appendix C, it can be expressed as

$$W''_{1,n}(\tau_o/2) = \sigma \sqrt{\Omega/2\pi}\; \theta \qquad (4\text{-}22)$$

where θ is a normal random variable. We assume that the output device reproduces the message corresponding to the first signal if

$$U_d > U_n = \frac{U_o}{\pi} \text{ Si } \frac{\Omega \tau_o}{2} \tag{4-23}$$

i. e., if U_d is less than half the rectified signal voltage at that moment, and otherwise reproduces the message corresponding to the second signal.

We now find the probability that the second message is reproduced instead of the first, i. e., the probability that U_d does not satisfy the inequality (4-23). This probability is

$$P(A_2 \text{ instead of } A_1) = P(U'_d < U_n) = P(\theta < -\beta) \tag{4-24}$$

where we have introduced the symbol

$$\beta = (U_o/\sigma)\,(1/\pi\Omega)^{1/2}\,\text{Si}(\Omega\tau_o/2) \tag{4-25}$$

according to Eq. (2-48), this means that

$$P(A_2 \text{ instead of } A_1) = V(\beta) \tag{4-26}$$

Similarly, we have

$$P(A_1 \text{ instead of } A_2) = P(U''_d > U_n) = P(\theta > \beta) = V(\beta) \tag{4-27}$$

It follows from Eqs. (4-26) and (4-27) that

$$P_E = V(\beta) \tag{4-28}$$

for the given means of reception.

To obtain the minimum probability of error, we must try to make β as large as possible. The dependence of β on the filter bandwidth Ω/π can be found by first rewriting Eq. (4-25) as

$$\beta = (U_o/\sigma)\,(\tau_o/2\pi)^{1/2}\,\frac{\text{Si } x}{\sqrt{x}} \tag{4-29}$$

where

$$x = \Omega\tau_o/2$$

The dependence of Si $x/\sqrt{x}$ on x is shown in Figure 4-3. As can be seen from the figure, this quantity has its maximum value of 1.14 for $x = 2.1$. Hence, for the given means of reception, the optimum filter bandwidth is

$$\Omega/\pi = 4.2/\pi\tau_o = 1.34/\tau_o \tag{4-30}$$

and the maximum value of β for this bandwidth is

$$\beta_{max} = 0.455\ U_o\sqrt{\tau_o}/\sigma = 0.91\ Q_1/\sqrt{2}\ \sigma \tag{4-31}$$

Thus, for the case considered in this section, the probability of error is determined by β, just as in the case of ideal reception it is determined by α, in accordance with (4-8). Comparing (4-31) and (4-16), we see that β_{max} is somewhat less than α, which means that even when the bandwidth is optimun, the means of reception we are considering gives somewhat larger error probabilities than would be obtained with the ideal receiver.

We now find the value of the efficiency coefficient (introduced in Section 4-2) for the means of reception under consideration. Clearly, in the present case, when the bandwidth is optimum, this coefficient equals

$$(\beta_{max}/\alpha)^2 = 0.83 \tag{4-32}$$

Thus, by using the ideal receiver, the signal energy can be lowered by a factor of 0.83 while keeping the same probability of error. It follows from this that the means of reception in question is very close to being ideal in its noise immunity.

4-6 Noise immunity for the classical telegraph signal and reception with an ordinary detector

We now consider the probability of error in the case where an ordinary detector is used instead of a synchronous detector in the receiver analyzed in the preceding section. In this case, the rectified voltage depends on the amplitude of the waveform which is the sum of the signal and noise at the filter output. Suppose that the receiver reproduces the first message if at the time $\tau_o/2$ this amplitude U_f at the filter output exceeds half the signal amplitude, i.e., if

$$U_f > (U_o/\pi)\ \mathrm{Si}(\Omega\tau_o/2) = U_n \tag{4-33}$$

and reproduces the second message if this inequality is not satisfied. Rice has calculated the probability that the amplitude of the sum of a sine wave and random noise is less than

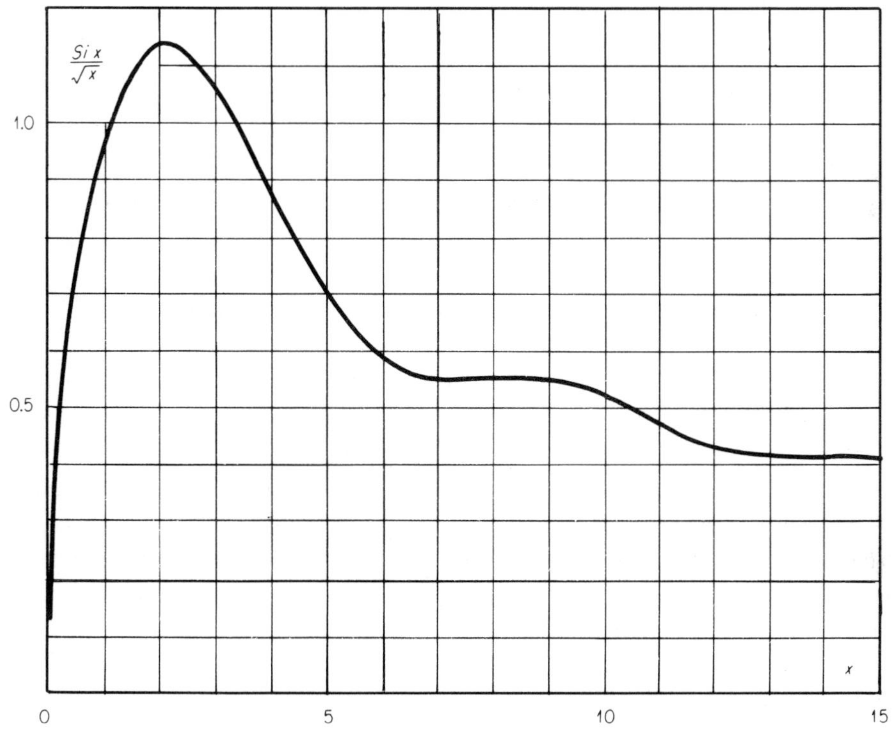

Fig. 4-3.

a given value[1]. Using his results, which he presented in the form of curves, we can calculate the value of the probability that at the time $\tau_o/2$ the amplitude of the sum of the signal and the noise is less than U_n, i.e., that an error occurs. We designate this probability by $P(A_2$ instead of $A_1)$. Then, we find the probability that the noise exceeds the value U_n in the absence of any signal disturbance, i.e., that the signal $A_2(t)$ is interpreted as the signal $A_1(t)$. This probability has been given by many authors including Rice[1], and is the integral from 0 to U_n of the Rayleigh distribution

$$P(A_1 \text{ instead of } A_2) = \exp(-U_n^2/2H^2) \qquad (4\text{-}34)$$

where H is the effective value of the noise, which, according to (2-57), is $\sigma\sqrt{\Omega/\pi}$ in our case. Substituting this value and the value of U_n into (4-34), we obtain

$$P(A_1 \text{ instead of } A_2) = \exp(-\beta^2/2) \qquad (4\text{-}35)$$

where β is defined by Eq. (4-25).

Assuming that the signals $A_1(t)$ and $A_2(t)$ are equally likely to be transmitted, we have for the probability of error

$$P_E = 0.5\, P(A_1 \text{ instead of } A_2) + 0.5\, P(A_2 \text{ instead of } A_1)$$

This probability is plotted as curve 3 in Figure 4-4 for the case of optimum bandwidth (given here also by Eq. (4-30)). Moreover, for comparison, we have indicated the probability of error for the case of reception with a synchronous detector (curve 2) and for the case of the ideal receiver (curve 1). In all cases we take as the abcissa the quantity $Q_1/\sqrt{2}\,\sigma$, where Q_1^2 is the specific energy given by Eq. (4-15). In Figure 4-5, curve 1 shows the dependence of the efficiency coefficient on P_E, for the kind of reception analyzed in this section. In this case, the efficiency coefficient is the square of the ratio of the abcissas of the curves 1 and 2 in Figure 4-4, taken at a given value of P_E. The straight line labelled 2 in this figure shows for comparison the value 0.83 of the efficiency coefficient for reception with a synchronous detector.

4-7 Results on the noise immunity of systems with a passive space

As just shown, the optimum noise immunity for constant noise intensity with this means of communication is completely determined by the quantity

$$Q_1^2 = T\, \overline{A_1^2(t)} \int_{-\infty}^{+\infty} A_1^2(t)\, dt$$

1. S. O. Rice, "Mathematical analysis of random noise", Bell Syst. Tech. J., 1944-5, Sect. 3-10.

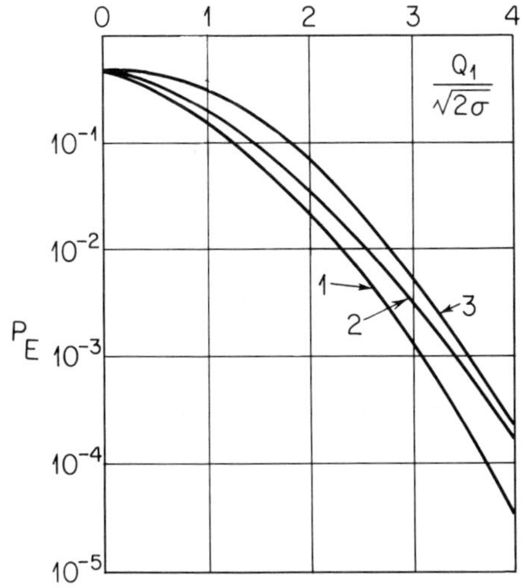

Fig. 4-4. Probability of error for the signal with rectangular envelope. Curve 1 -- ideal receiver; curve 2 -- synchronous receiver; curve 3 -- ordinary receiver; Q_1 is defined by Eq. (4-15). The two signals are equiprobable.

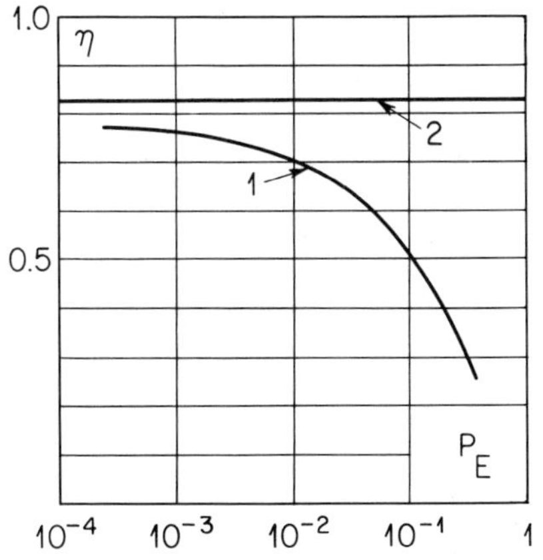

Fig. 4-5. Efficiency coefficient for the signal with rectangular envelope. Curve 1 -- ordinary receiver; curve 2 -- synchronous receiver. The two signals are equiprobable.

i.e., by the signal energy. The shape of the signal does not affect the optimum noise immunity. Using the classical telegraph signal and receivers with optimum bandwith (which were considered in Sections 4-5 and 4-6), we obtain a noise immunity which is quite close to optimum, and which is somewhat larger for the synchronous detector than for the ordinary detector. Thus, it follows that the application of methods of reception which differ from those considered in Sections 4-5 and 4-6 cannot substantially increase the noise immunity, when the signal energy is kept constant. This is the state of affairs provided that the shape, magnitude, and time of arrival of the signal are known, and the noise is of the normal fluctuation type. However, it cannot be inferred from this that one should always use the means of transmission and reception discussed here when dealing with telegraphy with a passive space. In many cases it can happen that other means of transmission and reception are more suitable, for example, because of the influence of fading, impulse noise, etc.

4-8 The optimum communication system with an active space

In this and the following sections, we shall consider the optimum noise immunity of systems in which the signals can take on two values $A_1(t)$ and $A_2(t)$, neither of which is identically zero. First of all, we try to find the optimum system, i.e., the one which furnishes the largest possible noise immunity for a given signal energy Q^2. To do this, it is clear that we should select signals for which the quantity

$$\alpha^2 = \frac{1}{2\sigma^2} \int_{-T/2}^{+T/2} (A_1(t) - A_2(t))^2 \, dt = \frac{1}{2\sigma^2} T \overline{(A_1(t) - A_2(t))^2} \tag{4-36}$$

which determines the optimum noise immunity is a maximum under the constraints

$$\int_{-T/2}^{+T/2} A_1^2(t) \, dt = T \overline{A_1^2(t)} \leq Q^2, \qquad \int_{-T/2}^{+T/2} A_2^2(t) \, dt = T \overline{A_2^2(t)} \leq Q^2 \tag{4-37}$$

Since we have

$$\int_{-T/2}^{+T/2} (A_1(t) - A_2(t))^2 \, dt = 2 \int_{-T/2}^{+T/2} A_1^2(t) \, dt + 2 \int_{-T/2}^{+T/2} A_2^2(t) \, dt - \int_{-T/2}^{+T/2} (A_1(t) + A_2(t))^2 \, dt$$

to obtain the maximum of this expression we must make the first two integrals as large as possible and the last integral as small as possible. The maximum value of the first two integrals which is consistent with the conditions (4-37) is obtained by taking

$$\int_{-T/2}^{+T/2} A_1^2(t) \, dt = \int_{-T/2}^{+T/2} A_2^2(t) \, dt = Q^2 \tag{4-38}$$

The third integral cannot take on negative values. Therefore, when

$$A_1(t) = - A_2(t) \tag{4-39}$$

it assumes its minimum value of zero. There is no contradiction between (4-38) and (4-39).

Thus α, and therefore the optimum noise immunity, is a maximum if $A_1(t)$ and $A_2(t)$ are equal in absolute value, opposite in sign, and have the maximum permissible signal energy. The shape of the signals has no influence on the optimum noise immunity, and can be arbitrary. For this optimum state of affairs, it is clear the quantity α, which determines the optimum noise immunity is equal to

$$\alpha^2 = \left[\frac{2}{\sigma^2} \int_{-T/2}^{+T/2} A_1^2(t)\, dt \right]^{1/2} = \sqrt{2}\; Q/\sigma \tag{4-40}$$

This value determines the optimum noise immunity which can be obtained for operation with an active space and an arbitrary system with two discrete signals, provided that the maximum signal energy is specified. Comparing the value of α just obtained with the value of α for operation with a passive space (as given by Eq. (4-12)), we see that in the optimum case we can decrease the specific signal energy Q^2 by a factor of 4, while keeping the same value of α, and consequently the same probability of error.

Suppose that for the signal $A_1(t)$ in the optimum system we take the signal given by Eq. (4-13), and use for the receiver an optimum bandwidth filter (given by Eq. (4-30)), a synchronous detector, and an output device which reproduces the first signal if the voltage on its terminals at time $\tau_o/2$ is positive, and the second signal if the voltage is negative. Then, the efficiency coefficient for reception is $\eta = 0.83$, as in the case considered in Section 4-5. This is easily seen by repeating in the present context the considerations of Section 4-5. We note that for this method of reception the noise immunity is close to the optimum.

4-9 Noise immunity for frequency shift keying

By frequency shift keying we mean transmission which uses the signals

$$\begin{aligned}
A_1(t) &= U_o \cos(\omega_1 t + \phi_1), && \text{for } 0 \le t \le \tau_o \\
A_1(t) &= 0, && \text{for } t < 0 \text{ or } t > \tau_o \\
A_2(t) &= U_o \cos(\omega_2 t + \phi_2) && \text{for } 0 \le t \le \tau_o \\
A_2(t) &= 0, && \text{for } t < 0 \text{ or } t > \tau_o
\end{aligned} \tag{4-41}$$

For this communication system

$$\alpha^2 = \frac{1}{2\sigma^2} \int_{-T/2}^{+T/2} (A_1(t) - A_2(t))^2 \, dt$$

$$= \frac{U_o^2}{2\sigma^2} \int_0^{\tau_o} \left\{ 1 + \frac{1}{2}\cos(2\omega_1 t + 2\phi_1) + \frac{1}{2}\cos(2\omega_2 t + 2\phi_2) - \cos\left[(\omega_1 + \omega_2)t + \phi_2 + \phi_2\right] - \cos\left[(\omega_1 - \omega_2)t + \phi_1 - \phi_2\right] \right\} dt$$

In doing the integral, the second, third, and fourth terms in the curly brackets give quantities which go to zero as ω_1 and ω_2 increase; we assume that ω_1 and ω_2 are large so that these terms can be neglected. Then after integration and some manipulation, we obtain

$$\alpha^2 = \frac{Q^2}{\sigma^2} \left\{ 1 - \frac{\sin\left[(\omega_1 - \omega_2)\tau_o + \phi_1 - \phi_2\right] - \sin(\phi_1 - \phi_2)}{(\omega_1 - \omega_2)\tau_o} \right\} \tag{4-42}$$

where

$$Q^2 = \frac{U_o^2 \tau_o}{2} \tag{4-43}$$

is the specific energy of the signals. The value of α so obtained depends on $\phi_1 - \phi_2$, the difference of the initial phases. If the frequency shift keying is produced by changing the circuit parameters of an oscillator, then $\phi_1 = \phi_2$, and the expression simplified. In this case we have

$$\alpha^2 = \frac{Q^2}{\sigma^2} \left\{ 1 - \frac{\sin(\omega_1 - \omega_2)\tau_o}{(\omega_1 - \omega_2)\tau_o} \right\} \tag{4-44}$$

The dependence of the expression in curly brackets on $(\omega_1 - \omega_2)\tau_o$ is shown in Figure 4-6. We can draw the following conclusions from an examination of this figure.

1. For the kind of operation in question, the largest optimum noise immunity is obtained for the frequency difference

$$\frac{(\omega_1 - \omega_2)}{2\pi} = \frac{0.7}{\tau_o} \tag{4-45}$$

For smaller differences, the optimum noise immunity becomes smaller. This circumstance allows one to determine the minimum frequency bandwidth below which one should not go if one wishes to avoid loss of noise immunity.

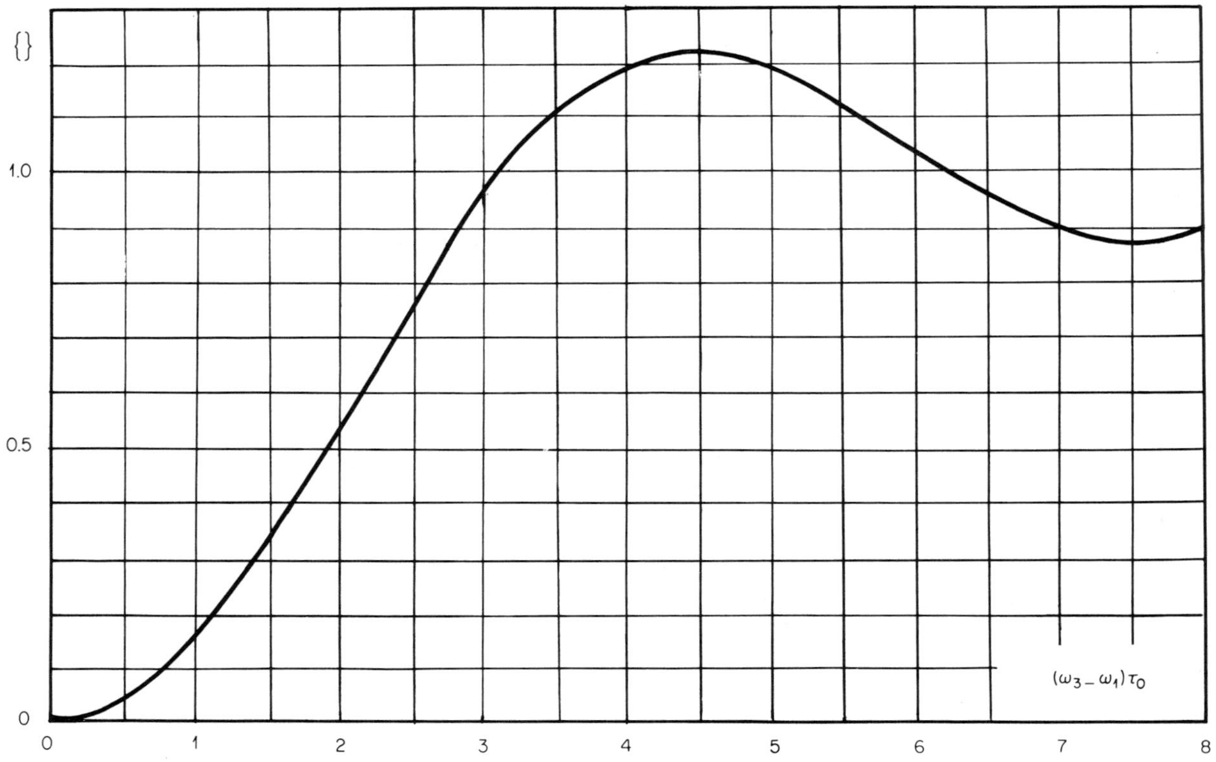

Fig. 4-6. The term in curly brackets in Eq. (4-44).

2. For the kind of operation in question, and for the optimum frequency difference, the value of α^2 is $1.2Q^2/\sigma^2$, i.e., 2.4 times larger than the value obtained for transmission with a passive space, if in both cases the specific signal energy Q^2 is identical. Thus, the optimum noise immunity for frequency shift keying is not much larger than the optimum noise immunity obtained for the operation with a passive space analyzed in Section 4-4. Moreover, if we bear in mind that in the latter case, according to Sections 4-5 and 4-6, we can come very close to the optimum noise immunity, then we are led to the conclusion that we cannot get appreciably more noise immunity with frequency shift keying (in the case of undistorted signals and normal fluctuation noise) than with classical amplitude modulation. The gain in noise immunity which is observed when changing from amplitude to frequency modulation (for short wave operation) must evidently be ascribed to signal distortion produced by fading.

4-10 Optimum noise immunity for normal fluctuation noise with frequency-dependent intensity

Until this section, we have considered normal fluctuation noise consisting of a large number of very short pulses which have a constant intensity. In Appendix D it is shown that noise consisting of pulses of arbitrary shape can be written as

$$W^*_{\mu,\nu}(t) = \sum_{i=\mu}^{\nu} \left[\frac{\sigma^*(i/T)}{\sqrt{T}} \left(\theta^*_{2i-1} \sin \frac{2\pi}{T} it + \theta^*_{2i} \cos \frac{2\pi}{T} it\right)\right] \tag{4-46}$$

if we take into account components with frequencies from μ/T to ν/T; here the θ^* are (mutually) independent normal random variables. This expression differs from (2-54) in that here the amplitude of a noise component depends on its frequency. We now explain how the case of the noise (4-46) can be reduced to the case considered previously.

Suppose that the received signal can again take on two values $A_1(t)$ and $A_2(t)$, and suppose that to the signal is added the noise $W^*_{\mu,\nu}(t)$ with the intensity $\sigma^*(f)$, which varies with the frequency. We use the receiver R prepared according to the scheme shown in Figure 4-7a. In this scheme B designates an equalizer, i.e., a linear device which has

$$k(f) = \frac{k_o}{\sigma^*(f)} \tag{4-47}$$

for the amplitude of its transfer function, where k_o is a constant. The phase of the equalizer transfer function can be arbitrary. In going through the equalizer, the noise will be altered; instead of the noise $W^*_{\mu,\nu}(t)$ with intensity $\sigma^*(f)$ acting at the point 1, we obtain at the point 2 the noise $W_{\mu,\nu}(t)$ which (according to Appendix D) is also normal fluctuation noise, but which has the intensity

$$\sigma_o = \sigma^*(f)\, k(f) = k_o$$

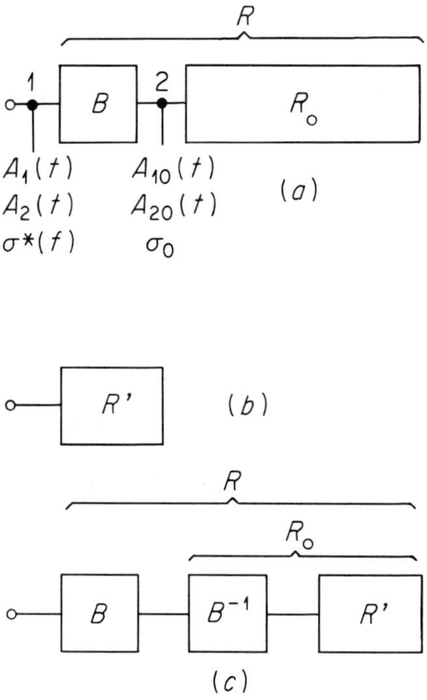

Fig. 4-7. R_o is the ideal receiver for the signals $A_{10}(t)$ and $A_{20}(t)$ and noise with constant intensity σ_o; R is the ideal receiver for the signals $A_1(t)$ and $A_2(t)$ and noise with intensity $\sigma^*(f)$; B is the four-pole with transfer coefficient K, where $|K| = \sigma_o/\sigma^*(f)$; B^{-1} is the four-pole with transfer coefficient K^{-1}.

i.e., constant intensity. The signals also change their form in going through the equalizer; let them have the forms $A_{10}(t)$ and $A_{20}(t)$ at the point 2. Clearly, the receiver R produces an error if and only if the receiver R_o produces an error. Thus, the probability of error of the receiver R for the signals $A_1(t)$ and $A_2(t)$ and for noise with intensity $\sigma^*(f)$ equals the probability of error of the receiver R_o for the signals $A_{10}(t)$ and $A_{20}(t)$ and for noise with intensity σ_o. Thus, in order for the receiver R to give the smallest probability of error, it is clear that we should choose the receiver R_o to be ideal in the sense of section 3-2.

The receiver R just obtained is ideal for reception of the signals $A_1(t)$ and $A_2(t)$ in the presence of noise with intensity $\sigma^*(f)$. Indeed, it gives the least possible probability of error for receivers constructed according to the scheme of Figure 4-7a, and moreover, this scheme can be used to construct a receiver with the same probability of error as any other receiver. In fact, an arbitrary receiver R' (see Figure 4-7b) is equivalent to the receiver shown in Figure 4-7c, where B^{-1} designates the linear four-pole inverse to the four-pole B, and the receiver with the diagram shown in Figure 4-7c reduces to a receiver with the diagram shown in Figure 4-7a. The optimum noise immunity is characterized by the probability of error of the ideal receiver just obtained. Obviously, this probability of error is that of an ideal receiver for the signals $A_{10}(t)$ and $A_{20}(t)$ and noise with the intensity σ_o, which is independent of frequency. The latter probability can be determined by the formulas of Section 4-1, if in these formulas we replace $A_1(t)$, $A_2(t)$, and σ by $A_{10}(t)$, $A_{20}(t)$, and σ_o, respectively.

In this section we have examined a method which takes into account variable noise intensity for the case of two discrete signals. This method also works for all the other cases considered below. Therefore, we shall hereafter not be concerned any more with this matter.

4-11 Geometric interpretation of the material of chapter 4

In the case of two discrete signals, the domains of the ideal receiver which correspond to these signals are determined by the inequality (4-1). If instead of the inequality sign, we write an equality, then the points corresponding to the waveforms X(t) defined by this equality will form a plane. This plane, which is perpendicular to the line joining the signal points $A_1(t)$ and $A_2(t)$ is a boundary plane, dividing the domains of the signals $A_1(t)$ and $A_2(t)$. In the case where the signals are equiprobable, the plane passes through the midpoint of the line joining $A_1(t)$ and $A_2(t)$. An error occurs when the noise vector adds to the radius vector of the transmitted signal and gives a resultant vector with a terminus lying on the other side of the boundary plane. Since all directions of the noise vector are equiprobable, it is natural that the probability of error depends only on the distance of the boundary plane from the signal points, or equivalently, on the distance between the signals, i.e., on the quantity $\overline{(A_1(t) - A_2(t))^2}$, as already shown.

In the case of transmission with a passive space, the radius vector of one of the signals is zero. In this case, the optimum noise immunity depends only on the quantity $\overline{A_1^2(t)}$, which determines the distance between the end of the radius vector of the signal $A_1(t)$ and the origin of coordinates. To find the optimum communication system (Section 4-8), we posed oursleves the problem of finding the system which uses two signals with radius vectors not exceeding a certain quantity in length, and which has the maximum distance between the ends of these vectors. Naturally, such a system is obtained by taking radius vectors of the maximum possible length, and then orienting them in opposite directions, i. e., by setting one of the vectors equal to the negative of the other.

CHAPTER 5

NOISE IMMUNITY FOR SIGNALS WITH MANY DISCRETE VALUES

5-1 General statement of the problem

In the preceding chapter we considered the noise immunity for the case where the signal can take on only two values. In this chapter we are concerned with a similar question, but for the more general case where the messages and therefore the signals can have m discrete values. Let these signal values be

$$A_1(t),\ A_2(t),\ \ldots\ ,\ A_m(t) \tag{5-1}$$

and let us find the probability of error for the reception of such signals with the ideal receiver considered in Chapter 3. This probability will obviously characterize the optimum noise immunity.

Suppose the signal $A_1(t)$ was sent. Then the waveform acting upon the receiver is

$$X(t) = W_{\mu,\nu}(t) + A_1(t) \tag{5-2}$$

Then clearly the receiver will reproduce the message corresponding to the transmitted signal $A_1(t)$ if (according to Section 3-2) we have

$$T\ \overline{(X(t) - A_1(t))^2} - \sigma^2 \ln P(A_1) < T\ \overline{(X(t) - A_j(t))^2} - \sigma^2 \ln P(A_j) \tag{5-3}$$

for all $j = 2, \ldots, m$. An error occurs if even one of the inequalities (5-3) is not satisfied. Substituting the value of $X(t)$ from (5-2) into Eq. (5-3), we obtain after some manipulation

$$2T\ \overline{W_{\mu,\nu}(t)(A_j(t) - A_1(t))} < T\ \overline{(A_j(t) - A_1(t))^2} + \sigma^2 \ln \frac{P(A_1)}{P(A_j)} \tag{5-4}$$

The probability that this system of inequalities is fulfilled is the probability of correct reception of the signal $A_1(t)$ with an ideal receiver. Similar relations obtain for the other signals. In the general case, the size of this probability is given by integrals which are not evaluated. Therefore, in what follows we shall examine only the most interesting special cases.

5-2 Optimum noise immunity for orthogonal equiprobable signals with the same energy

We now consider the case where

$$T\ \overline{A_i^2(t)} = Q^2, \qquad \overline{A_i(t)\,A_j(t)} = 0, \qquad P(A_i) = \frac{1}{m} \tag{5-5}$$

for i, j = 1, 2, ... , m, but i $\neq$ j. In this case, using (2-60) and (2-61), we easily reduce the inequality (5-4) to

$$\sigma\sqrt{2T}\sqrt{\overline{A_j^2(t)}}\,\theta_j - \sigma\sqrt{2T}\sqrt{\overline{A_1^2(t)}}\,\theta_1 < T\,(\overline{A_j^2(t)} + \overline{A_1^2(t)})$$

or

$$\theta_j - \theta_1 < \sqrt{2}\,Q/\sigma \qquad (5\text{-}6)$$

for j = 2, 3, ... , m, where the θ_j are (mutually) independent normal random variables. Suppose θ_1 satisfies the condition

$$y < \theta_1 < y + dy \qquad (5\text{-}7)$$

According to (2-34), the probability of this is

$$\frac{dy}{\sqrt{2\pi}}\exp(-\frac{y^2}{2}) \qquad (5\text{-}8)$$

In this case, for the j'th inequality (5-6) to be satisfied, we must have

$$\theta_j < \frac{\sqrt{2}\,Q}{\sigma} + y \qquad (5\text{-}9)$$

According to (2-48), the probability of this is

$$1 - V\left(\frac{\sqrt{2}\,Q}{\sigma} + y\right) \qquad (5\text{-}10)$$

Since all the θ_j are independent, the probability that all the m-1 inequalities (5-6) and the inequality (5-7) are simultaneously fulfilled is

$$\frac{dy}{\sqrt{2\pi}}\exp\left(-\frac{y^2}{2}\right)\left[1 - V\left(\frac{\sqrt{2}\,Q}{\sigma} + y\right)\right]^{m-1} \qquad (5\text{-}11)$$

From this it follows that the probability that all the inequalities (5-6) are satisfied for arbitrary θ_1 is

$$P(A_1\ \text{correct}) = \frac{1}{\sqrt{2\pi}}\int_{-\infty}^{+\infty}\left[1 - V\left(\frac{\sqrt{2}\,Q}{\sigma} + y\right)\right]^{m-1}\exp(-\frac{y^2}{2})\,dy \qquad (5\text{-}12)$$

This probability is the probability that the transmitted signal $A_1(t)$ is correctly interpreted by the ideal receiver. In the case under consideration, this probability is the same for all the symbols and characterizes the optimum noise immunity.

5-3 Example of telegraphy using 32 orthogonal signals

On the basis of the theory presented in the preceding section, we now calculate the optimum noise immunity for the case of telegraphic communication where the signals characterizing the separate letters all have the same energy Q^2 and are orthogonal to one another. This will be the case if the letters are transmitted as sine waves which have the same amplitude U_o and duration τ_o for all the letters, but a different frequency for each letter. Under these conditions, the waveform representing the k'th letter is

$$A_k(t) = U_o \cos(\omega_k t + \phi) \quad \text{for} \quad 0 \leq t \leq \tau_o$$
$$A_k(t) = 0 \quad \text{for} \quad t < 0 \text{ or } t > \tau_o \qquad (5\text{-}13)$$

The scalar product of the waveform $A_k(t)$ and the waveform $A_i(t)$ corresponding to the i'th letter is equal to

$$\overline{A_k(t)\,A_i(t)} = \frac{1}{T}\int_{-T/2}^{+T/2} A_k(t)\,A_i(t)\,dt$$

$$= \frac{U_o^2}{2T}\left[\frac{\sin(\omega_k - \omega_i)\tau_o}{\omega_k - \omega_i} + \frac{\sin[(\omega_k+\omega_i)\tau_o + 2\phi] - \sin 2\phi}{\omega_k + \omega_i}\right] \qquad (5\text{-}14)$$

If we assume that $(\omega_k - \omega_i)\tau_o/2\pi$ and $(\omega_k + \omega_i)\tau_o/2\pi$ are integers, then the waveforms $A_k(t)$ and $A_i(t)$ are orthogonal, since the expression (5-14) will then vanish. Obviously, these waveforms can also be regarded as orthogonal if $(\omega_k - \omega_i)\tau_o/2\pi$ is an integer and $\omega_k + \omega_i \gg |\omega_k - \omega_i|$. Thus, the signals are orthogonal if their frequencies are separated from one another by multiples of $1/\tau_o$, and if their sums are much greater than their differences. The signals are also orthogonal if the separate letters are transmitted as arbitrary waveforms which do not overlap, for in this case obviously

$$\overline{A_i(t)\,A_k(t)} = \frac{1}{T}\int_{-T/2}^{+T/2} A_i(t)\,A_k(t)\,dt = 0 \qquad (5\text{-}15)$$

since for any t at least one of the factors inside the integral vanishes. Furthermore, if we assume that the probability of transmission of each of the signals is the same and that $m = 32$, then by numerical integration of Eq. (5-12), we obtain the result represented by curve 1 in Figure 5-1, where the quantity Q/σ is plotted as the abcissa, and the probability $P_E = 1 - P(A_i \text{ correct})$ is plotted as the ordinate. Later we shall compare the probability of error obtained in this way with the probability of error for other means of communication.

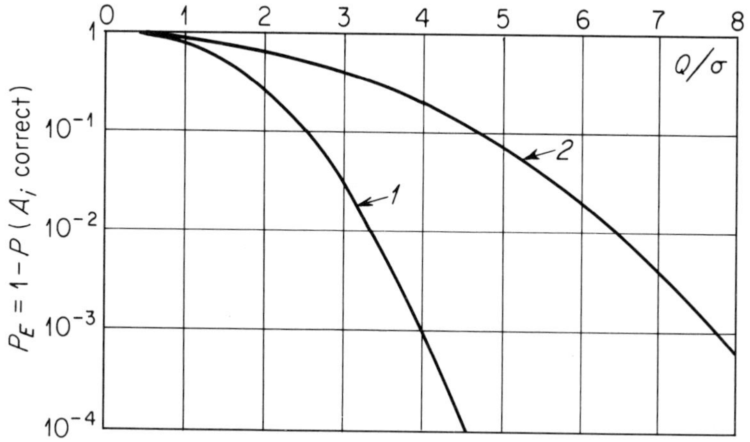

Fig. 5-1. Probability of error with the ideal receiver for 32 signals with the same a priori probability. Curve 1 -- transmission of orthogonal signals; curve 2 -- transmission of five two-valued pulses.

5-4 Optimum noise immunity for compound signals

Very often complicated signals consist of a sequence of simpler signals. Thus, for example, in telegraphy the signals corresponding to the letters and characters almost always consist of separate two-valued elementary signals which follow each other in sequence and have the same length. We now find the optimum noise immunity for such signals. We begin with the general case.

Suppose that the first elementary signal which makes up the compound signal can have one of the following values:

$$B_1(t),\ B_2(t),\ \ldots\ ,\ B_m(t) \tag{5-16}$$

Suppose that the second elementary signal begins at a time τ after the beginning of the first signal. Then it will obviously have one of the following values:

$$B_1(t-\tau),\ B_2(t-\tau),\ \ldots\ ,\ B_m(t-\tau) \tag{5-17}$$

Finally, the ℓ'th elementary signal will have one of the following values:

$$B_1(t-\ell\tau+\tau),\ B_2(t-\ell\tau+\tau),\ \ldots\ ,\ B_m(t-\ell\tau+\tau) \tag{5-18}$$

If the compound signal consists of n elementary signals, then clearly it has the following form:

$$B_{k1}(t) + B_{k2}(t-\tau) + \cdots + B_{kn}(t - n\tau + \tau) \tag{5-19}$$

where $k_1, \ldots, k_n$ are certain integers which can take on values from 1 to m, depending on which compound signal is sent. In the case under consideration, the compound signal can have m^n values. We assume that the separate elementary signals which follow each other in sequence do not overlap. Under these conditions $B_i(t-k\tau)$ and $B_j(t-\ell\tau)$ will be orthogonal for arbitrary $k \neq \ell$, as was shown in the preceding section.

We now find the probability of error for the compound signal considered here, when it is received on an ideal receiver. Obviously, for the compound signal in question to be received without error by the ideal receiver, it is necessary and sufficient that all the elementary signals of which it consists be received without error by the receiver. We now show that errors in the separate elementary signals are independent under the conditions being considered and for reception with the ideal receiver. In fact, according to Section 5-1, if the ℓ'th elementary signal has the form

$$B_i(t-\ell\tau+\tau),$$

then it will be received without error on the ideal receiver provided that the noise has values such that the random variables

$$\overline{W_{\mu,\nu}(t)\,[B_j(t-\ell\tau+\tau) - B_i(t-\ell\tau+\tau)]} \qquad j = 1, 2, \ldots, m \tag{5-20}$$

have values satisfying the inequalities

$$2T\,\overline{W_{\mu,\nu}(t)\,[B_j(t-\ell\tau+\tau) - B_i(t-\ell\tau+\tau)]} < T\,\overline{[B_j(t-\ell\tau+\tau) - B_i(t-\ell\tau+\tau)]^2} + \sigma^2 \ln \frac{P(B_i)}{P(B_j)} \tag{5-21}$$

Moreover, the k'th elementary signal, which we assume has the value

$$B_{i'}(t-k\tau+\tau)$$

will be received without error if the random variables

$$\overline{W_{\mu,\nu}(t)\,[B_j(t-k\tau+\tau) - B_{i'}(t-k\tau+\tau)]} \tag{5-22}$$

have values satisfying the inequalities

$$2T\,\overline{W_{\mu,\nu}(t)\,[B_j(t-k\tau+\tau) - B_{i'}(t-k\tau+\tau)]} < T\,\overline{[B_j(t-k\tau+\tau) - B_{i'}(t-k\tau+\tau)]^2} + \sigma^2 \ln \frac{P(B_{i'})}{P(B_j)} \tag{5-23}$$

Since the functions in the square brackets in the expressions (5-20) and (5-22) are orthogonal, then, according to Section 2-4, these expressions are mutually independent random variables, which means also that the inequalities (5-21) and (5-23) are satisfied independently of each other. This proves the statement made about the independence of the error probabilities of the separate elementary signals.

The probability of correct reception of each elementary signal can be determined by the methods presented earlier. Obviously, in the case being considered, these probabilities are the same for all elementary signals (we assume that their a priori probabilities are the same) and are denoted by P (corr. elem.). Since as remarked, errors in the separate elementary signals are independent of each other, then obviously, the probability that all n elementary signals which form one compound signal are correctly received, i.e., that the compound signal is correctly received, has the form

$$1 - P_E = [P(\text{corr. elem.})]^n \tag{5-24}$$

5-5 Example of a five-valued code

We now apply the theory of the preceding section to f. m. telegraphy using a five-valued code. In this communication system, the signal corresponding to one character consists of five elementary signals, which follow one another in sequence, and each of which has the form discussed in Section 4-9. We shall assume that the probabilities of both values of the elementary signal are the same. In this case

$$P(\text{error elem.}) = V(\alpha) \tag{5-25}$$

where α is defined by Eq. (4-44), and

$$\alpha^2 = Q_n^2/\sigma^2 \tag{5-26}$$

where Q_n^2 is the energy of the elementary signal, provided that the frequency difference is such that the term in curly brackets in Eq. (4-44) equals unity. For this means of communication, the signal can have $m^n = 2^5 = 32$ different versions.

We now compare the optimum noise immunity for the signals in question with the noise immunity for the orthogonal signals studied in Section 5-3, which can also have 32 different versions. To do this, we express Q_n^2 in terms of the specific energy of the whole signal by writing $Q^2 = 5Q^2$. We obtain

$$\alpha^2 = 0.2Q^2/\sigma^2 \tag{5-27}$$

whence, according to Eqs. (5-24) and (5-27), the probability of error of the compound signal is

$$P_E = 1 - [P(\text{corr. elem.})]^n = 1 - [1 - V(\sqrt{0.2}\,Q/\sigma)]^5 \tag{5-28}$$

The value of this quantity is given by curve 2 in Figure 5-1, where Q/σ is plotted as the abcissa and P_E as the ordinate. Comparing this curve with curve 1 of the same figure, which gives the probability of error for a similar system with orthogonal signals, we see that the orthogonal system is more advantageous. To obtain the same probability of error with the orthogonal system, we need a signal energy as much as 3.5 times less than with the compound signal. On the other hand, the bandwidth occupied by the compound signal is approximately 3 times less, since in this case instead of 32 frequencies we need transmit only two frequencies, and moreover, the signals on these two frequencies have to be only 5 times shorter than in the case of the orthogonal signals.

5-6 The optimum system for signals with many discrete values

We now find the optimum system containing m signals, just as in Section 4-8 we found the optimum system containing two signals. Suppose we have a system of equiprobable signals

$$A_1(t), A_2(t), \ldots, A_m(t) \tag{5-29}$$

We shall show how to decrease the average energy of these signals without changing the optimum noise immunity. The optimum noise immunity is defined by the probability that the inequalities (5-4), which involve the signal differences, are satisfied. Thus, if we introduce the new signals

$$A'_k(t) = A_k(t) + B(t) \tag{5-30}$$

then the inequalities (5-4) are not changed, which means that the optimum noise immunity for the signals $A_k(t)$ and $A'_k(t)$ is the same. Geometrically, this means that if all the points corresponding to the signals undergo parallel translations by the same amount, then the distances between them and the optimum noise immunity determined by these distances, do not change.

We now find what the waveform $B(t)$ should be to make the average signal energy

$$Q^2_{av} = \frac{T}{m} \sum_{k=1}^{m} \overline{A'^2_k(t)} \tag{5-31}$$

a minimum. Using (5-30), we obtain

$$Q^2_{av} = \frac{T}{m} \left\{ \sum_{k=1}^{m} \overline{A^2_k(t)} + 2 \overline{\left[\sum_{k=1}^{m} A_k(t) \right] B(t)} + m \overline{B^2(t)} \right\} \tag{5-32}$$

If we change $B(t)$ while keeping $\overline{B^2(t)}$ constant, then the first and last terms in the curly brackets do not change, and a minimum is obtained when $B(t)$ has the opposite sign to $\sum_{k=1}^{m} A_k(t)$, i.e., when

$$B(t) = -\lambda \sum_{k=1}^{m} A_k(t)$$

where λ is a positive number. Substituting this value of $B(t)$ into (5-32), we obtain

$$Q^2_{av} = \frac{T}{m} \left\{ \sum_{k=1}^{m} \overline{A^2_k(t)} - (2\lambda - m\lambda^2) \overline{\left[\sum_{k=1}^{m} A_k(t) \right]^2} \right\} \tag{5-33}$$

Since in this equality the expressions under the overbars are always positive, Q_{av}^2 is a minimum when $2\lambda - m\lambda^2$ is a maximum, i.e., when $\lambda = 1/m$. Thus, to make the average energy of the signals $A_k'(t)$ a minimum without changing the noise immunity, we must take

$$A_i'(t) = A_i(t) - \frac{1}{m} \sum_{k=1}^{m} A_k(t) \tag{5-34}$$

It follows easily from this relation that

$$\sum_{k=1}^{m} A_k'(t) = 0 \tag{5-35}$$

We now study the system with m signals which has the minimum average energy for a given optimum noise immunity. If we assume that all the signals are equiprobable, and have the same probability of being correctly received, we can stipulate that such a system consists of signals which are equidistant from one another. Take an arbitrary system of signals which are equidistant from one another, say the system

$$B_1(t),\ B_2(t),\ \ldots\ ,\ B_m(t) \tag{5-36}$$

for which

$$T\ \overline{(B_i(t) - B_k(t))^2} = \beta^2 \tag{5-37}$$

independently of i and k ($i \neq k$). We now ascertain how much the energy of the signals of the system can be decreased without changing its optimum noise immunity. We form the system of signals

$$B_i'(t) = B_i(t) - \frac{1}{m} \sum_{k=1}^{m} B_k(t) \tag{5-38}$$

As already shown, this system has the same optimum noise immunity as the system of signals $B_i(t)$. The energy of the signal $B_1'(t)$ of this system is

$$
\begin{aligned}
T\ \overline{B_1'^2(t)} &= \frac{T}{m^2}\ \overline{[(m-1)\, B_1(t) - B_2(t) - \cdots - B_m(t)]^2} \\
&= \frac{T}{m^2}\ [(m-1)^2\, \overline{B_1^2(t)} + \overline{B_2^2(t)} + \cdots + \overline{B_m^2(t)} - 2(m-1)\, \overline{B_1(t)\, B_2(t)} \\
&\quad - 2(m-1)\, \overline{B_1(t)\, B_3(t)} - \cdots - 2(m-1)\, \overline{B_1(t)\, B_m(t)} \\
&\quad + 2\overline{B_2(t)\, B_3(t)} + 2\overline{B_2(t)\, B_4(t)} + \cdots + 2\overline{B_2(t)\, B_m(t)} \\
&\quad + 2\overline{B_3(t)\, B_4(t)} + \cdots + 2\overline{B_3(t)\, B_m(t)} + \\
&\quad \cdots\cdots\cdots \\
&\quad + 2\overline{B_{m-1}(t)\, B_m(t)}\ ]
\end{aligned}
$$

Moreover, bearing in mind that

$$2\overline{B_i(t)\,B_k(t)} = \overline{B_i^2(t)} + \overline{B_k^2(t)} - \overline{(B_i(t) - B_k(t))^2} = \overline{B_i^2(t)} + \overline{B_k^2(t)} - \beta^2/T \qquad (5\text{-}39)$$

we obtain after some simplification

$$T\,\overline{B_1'^2(t)} = \frac{m-1}{2m}\beta^2 = Q_{B'}^2 \qquad (5\text{-}40)$$

and similarly,

$$T\,\overline{B_i'^2(t)} = \frac{m-1}{2m}\beta^2 = Q_{B'}^2 \qquad (5\text{-}41)$$

Thus, <u>all the signals $B_i'(t)$ have the same energy $Q_{B'}^2$</u>.

To find the optimum noise immunity for this system, we form the system

$$B_i''(t) = B_i'(t) + C(t) \qquad (5\text{-}42)$$

taking $C(t)$ to be orthogonal to all the $B_i'(t)$. Moreover, let us choose $C(t)$ so that all the signals $B_i''(t)$ are mutually orthogonal, i.e., so that the equalities

$$\overline{B_i''(t)\,B_k''(t)} = \overline{B_i'(t)\,B_k'(t)} + \overline{C^2(t)} = 0, \qquad i \neq k$$

are fulfilled. To do this, we must have

$$\overline{C^2(t)} = -\overline{B_i'(t)\,B_k'(t)} = \frac{1}{2}\overline{(B_i'(t) - B_k'(t))^2} - \frac{1}{2}\overline{B_i'^2(t)} - \frac{1}{2}\overline{B_k'^2(t)}$$

But we have

$$\overline{(B_i'(t) - B_k'(t))^2} = \overline{(B_i(t) - B_k(t))^2} = \beta^2/T \qquad (5\text{-}43)$$

so that

$$T\,\overline{C^2(t)} = \frac{\beta^2}{2} - \frac{m-1}{2m}\beta^2 = \frac{\beta^2}{2m} \qquad (5\text{-}44)$$

Thus, we can always choose $C(t)$ so that the signals $B_i''(t)$ are mutually orthogonal. For this system, the energy of the signals is

$$Q_{B''}^2 = T\,\overline{B_i''^2(t)} = T\,\overline{B_i'^2(t)} + T\,\overline{C^2(t)} = \beta^2/2 \qquad (5\text{-}45)$$

Thus, the signals $B_i''(t)$ have the same energy and are orthogonal. We have already found the optimum noise immunity for such signals. It is given by Eq. (5-12), where in this case we must substitute

$$Q^2 = Q_{B''}^2 = \frac{1}{2}\beta^2 \qquad (5\text{-}46)$$

The systems of signals $B_i'(t)$ and $B_i''(t)$ have the same optimum noise immunity.

Thus, all systems of m signals which are equidistant from one another (have the same β) have the same optimum noise immunity. Systems of this type which have been obtained by the transformation (5-38) have the least possible average signal energy given by (5-41). These are the optimum systems (at least among the family of systems of equidistant signals). The optimum system of signals $B_i''(t)$ given by (5-38) can be formed from an arbitrary equidistant system $B_i(t)$, for example, from an arbitrary system of orthogonal signals which have equal energies. The optimum system is somewhat better than the orthogonal system. Indeed, for the same optimum noise immunity, the signal energy in the optimum system has to be

$$Q^2_{B'} = \frac{m-1}{2m} \beta^2 \tag{5-47}$$

whereas in the orthogonal system it is

$$Q^2 = Q^2_{B''} = \beta^2/2 \tag{5-48}$$

i.e., $m/(m-1)$ times larger. However, for large m, this difference is negligible. The system considered in Section 4-8 is the special case of the optimum system for $m = 2$.

5-7 Approximate evaluation of optimum noise immunity

The method of calculating optimum noise immunity discussed in Section 5-1 is often of little practical use, since in concrete problems the calculation of the probability that the inequalities (5-4) are satisfied presents great mathematical difficulties in many cases. Therefore, it is sometimes useful to have available a simple method of obtaining an approximate value of this probability. We now discuss this method.

In order for an error to occur when the signal $A_i(t)$ is sent, it is necessary that one or more of the inequalities (5-4) fails to be satisfied, where we replace the index 1 by i. Alternatively, it is necessary that one or more of the reverse inequalities be satisfied; these reverse inequalities can be written after some manipulation as

$$\sigma \sqrt{2T} \sqrt{\overline{(A_j(t) - A_i(t))^2}}\, \theta_{ij} > T\, \overline{(A_j(t) - A_i(t))^2} + \sigma^2 \ln \frac{P(A_i)}{P(A_j)}$$

$$j = 1, 2, \dots, m, \quad i \neq j \tag{5-49}$$

According to (2-47), the probability that the j'th of these inequalities is satisfied is equal to

$$P_{ij} = P(\theta_{ij} > \alpha_{ij}) = V(\alpha_{ij}) \tag{5-50}$$

where

$$\alpha_{ij} = \frac{\sqrt{T\ \overline{(A_j(t) - A_i(t))^2}}}{\sqrt{2}\,\sigma} + \frac{1}{2}\ \ln \frac{P(A_i)}{P(A_j)}\ \frac{\sqrt{2}\,\sigma}{\sqrt{T\ \overline{(A_j(t) - A_i(t))^2}}} \tag{5-51}$$

As is well known from probability theory, the probability P that one or more of the events $E_1, E_2, \ldots, E_m$ occurs always lies between the bounds

$$P(E_k)_{max} \leq P \leq \sum_{k=1}^{m} P(E_k)$$

where $P(E_k)$ is the probability of the event E_k, and $P(E_k)_{max}$ is the largest of the probabilities $P(E_1), P(E_2), \ldots, P(E_m)$. Here P equals the quantity on the left side of the inequality if the occurrence of one of the events necessarily implies that of the other events, and P equals the quantity on the right side of the inequality if the events $E_1, \ldots, E_m$ are mutually exclusive. Using this, we can conclude that the probability $P_E(A_i)$ that one or more of the inequalities (5-49) is satisfied, or equivalently, that the transmitted signal $A_i(t)$ is incorrectly received, satisfies the inequality

$$(P_{ij})_{max} \leq P_E(A_i) \leq \sum_{j=1}^{m} P_{ij} \tag{5-52}$$

where P_{ij} is defined by (5-50) and $(P_{ij})_{max}$ is the maximum value of P_{ij} when the index j ranges from 1 to m. We note that in the inequality (5-52) the term P_{ii} should be omitted, since $i \neq j$ in (5-49). This is accomplished automatically by setting $P_{ii} = 0$. Multiplying the inequality (5-52) by the probability that the signal $A_i(t)$ is transmitted, which we designate by $P(A_i)$, and adding the resulting equations for $i = 1, \ldots, m$, we obtain

$$\sum_{i=1}^{m} (P_{ij})_{max}\, P(A_i) \leq P_E \leq \sum_{i=1}^{m} \sum_{j=1}^{m} P(A_i)\, P_{ij} \tag{5-53}$$

where

$$P_E = \sum_{i=1}^{m} P_E(A_i)\, P(A_i) \tag{5-54}$$

is the probability of error for the signals in question and for reception with the ideal receiver.

5-8 Example of the transmission of numerals by Morse code

As an illustration of the method used in the preceding section, we determine the optimum noise immunity for the transmission of numerals with the use of Morse code. Here we shall assume that the amplitude of the signals is U_o, that the length of a dot is τ_o, that the length of a dash is $3\tau_o$, and that the space between a dot and a dash in one numeral is also τ_o. We shall assume that the probability of transmission is the same for the various numerals.

We denote the signal corresponding to the numeral 0 by $A_o(t)$, to 1 by $A_1(t)$, to 2 by $A_2(t)$, ... , to 9 by $A_9(t)$. Then, as can easily be verified, if we subtract the value of the signal corresponding to the numeral j from the value of the signal corresponding to the numeral i, and if we assume that the initial times of the signals coincide and that the frequency of the waveform is much greater than $1/\tau_o$, we obtain

$$T\ \overline{(A_j(t) - A_i(t))^2} = \nu_{ij}\, U_o^2\, \tau_o \qquad (5\text{-}55)$$

where the ν_{ij} are given in Table 5-1. Thus, according to Eq. (5-51), for this case we have

$$\alpha_{ij} = \sqrt{\frac{\nu_{ij}\, U_o^2\, \tau_o}{2\sigma^2}} = \sqrt{\nu_{ij}}\ \alpha'$$

where

$$\alpha' = \sqrt{\tau_o/2}\ U_o/\sigma \qquad (5\text{-}56)$$

whence it follows that

$$P_{ij} = V(\sqrt{\nu_{ij}}\ \alpha') \qquad \text{for } j \neq i \qquad (5\text{-}57)$$

and $P_{ii} = 0$, as already pointed out. On the basis of this data we can construct Table 5-2, where we have written

$$P_n = V(\sqrt{n}\ \alpha') \qquad (5\text{-}58)$$

Then, keeping in mind that in this case $P(A_o) = P(A_1) = \cdots = P(A_9) = 0.1$ and applying Eq. (5-5), we obtain

$$0.8P_1 + 0.2P_2 \leq P_E \leq 1.8P_1 + 2.8P_2 + 1.6P_3 + 2.2P_4 + 0.6P_5 \qquad (5\text{-}59)$$

j \ i	1	2	3	4	5	6	7	8	9	0
1	—	4	2	4	4	4	4	4	4	5
2	4	—	3	2	3	3	2	1	1	2
3	2	3	—	2	2	2	2	3	4	5
4	4	2	2	—	1	1	2	2	3	4
5	4	3	2	1	—	1	2	3	4	5
6	4	3	2	1	1	—	1	2	3	4
7	4	2	2	2	2	1	—	1	2	3
8	4	1	3	2	3	2	1	—	1	2
9	4	1	4	3	4	3	2	1	—	1
0	5	2	5	4	5	4	3	2	1	—

Table 5-1

i	$(P_{ij})_{max}$	$\sum_{j=0, j \neq i}^{9} P_{ij}$
1	P_2	$P_2 \qquad 7P_4 + P_5$
2	P_1	$2P_1 + 3P_2 + 3P_3 + P_4$
3	P_2	$5P_2 + 2P_3 + P_4 + P_5$
4	P_1	$2P_1 + 4P_2 + P_3 + 2P_4$
5	P_1	$2P_1 + 2P_2 + 2P_3 + 2P_4 + P_5$
6	P_1	$3P_1 + 2P_2 + 2P_3 + 2P_4$
7	P_1	$2P_1 + 5P_2 + P_3 + P_4$
8	P_1	$3P_1 + 3P_2 + 2P_3 + P_4$
9	P_1	$3P_1 + P_2 + 2P_3 + 3P_4$
0	P_1	$P_1 + 2P_2 + P_3 + 2P_4 + 3P_5$

The bounds for P_E, the probability of incorrect reception of a numeral, given by these inequalities, are displayed as functions of α' in Figure 5-2. As is evident from the figure, the bounds for P_E lie quite close together. These curves allow us to determine the average percentage of incorrectly received numerals for the case of the ideal receiver, for a given signal to noise ratio, and for a given keying speed (on which the quantity τ_o depends). If we carry out articulation experiments involving the reception by ear of signals representing numerals in the presence of noise of the fluctuation type, then the percentage of numerals which are incorrectly written down must be higher than $100P_E$, as determined from Figure 5-2. By comparing these data, we can determine how close the noise immunity for aural reception is to the optimum noise immunity, i.e., how much one can hope to increase the noise immunity of this kind of communication by improving reception.

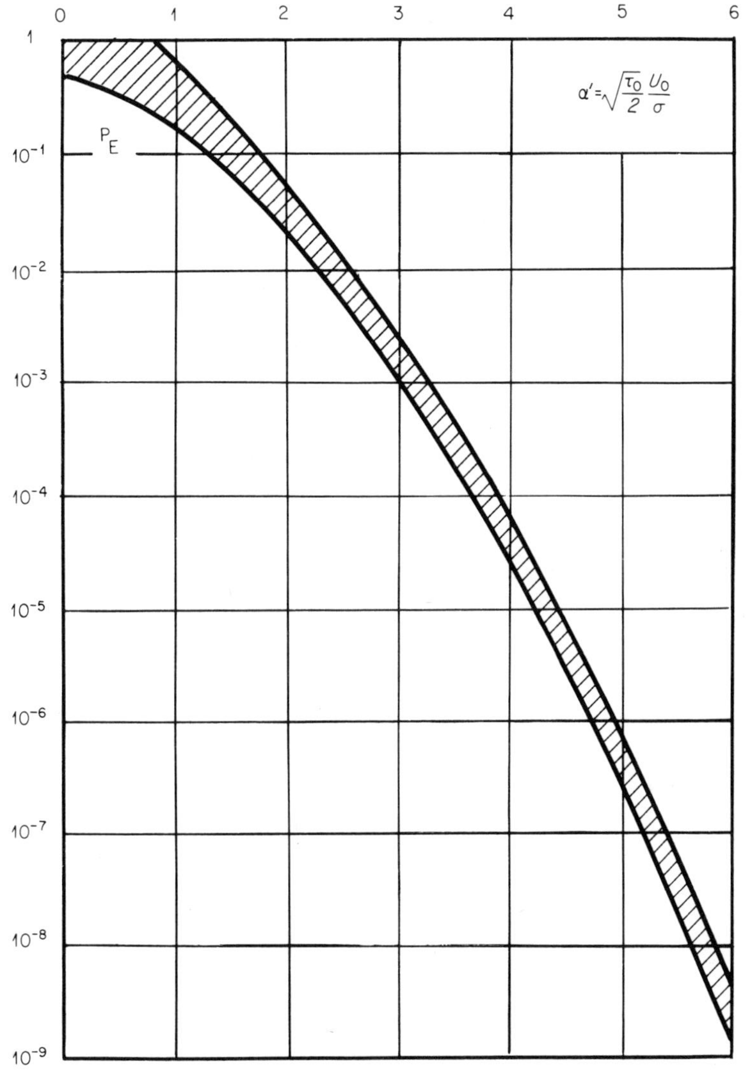

Fig. 5-2. Bounds for the probability of error with the ideal receiver for numerals transmitted by Morse code; τ_0 is the length and U_0 the amplitude of the elementary signal.

PART III
TRANSMISSION OF SEPARATE PARAMETER VALUES

CHAPTER 6
GENERAL THEORY OF THE INFLUENCE OF NOISE ON THE TRANSMISSION OF SEPARATE PARAMETER VALUES

6-1 General considerations

In the preceding chapters we considered the transmission of discrete messages and signals. In this part we shall consider the transmission of a message which is a parameter which can take on any value within certain limits, and where the parameter is not transmitted continuously in time, but has its instantaneous values transmitted at certain time intervals, with a different signal being used for the transmission of each value. For example, in telemetering we have to deal with transmission of this type. In this case the signal is a function of time and of the transmitted parameter λ, which is a constant for a given signal. We shall write such a signal as

$$A(\lambda, t) \qquad (6\text{-}1)$$

If the noise $W_{\mu,\nu}(t)$ is added to this signal, then the waveform acting on the receiver is

$$X(t) = W_{\mu,\nu}(t) + A(\lambda, t) \qquad (6\text{-}2)$$

Clearly, we would get the same waveform $X(t)$ if another parameter, say λ', was transmitted and if the noise took on a value $W'_{\mu,\nu}(t)$ such that

$$W'_{\mu,\nu}(t) + A(\lambda', t) = X(t) \qquad (6\text{-}3)$$

This is always possible, since as already remarked, normal fluctuation noise assumes any value with some probability. It follows from what has been said that in the presence of noise one can never determine with certainty from the received signal what value of the parameter λ was transmitted.

In this chapter we shall determine the probability of the transmitted parameter having some value or other, when the received waveform is known. We shall find out what property the receiver should have in order to reproduce the most probable parameter value, given a received waveform. We shall call such a receiver ideal. Then we shall find the amount of error obtained when the ideal receiver is used to reproduce the parameter. We shall show that the mean square error has the smallest possible value for the ideal receiver, and we shall find this smallest value. This least possible error will depend on the signal form, and will characterize the optimum noise immunity for the given signal. The material considered in this part will also be used extensively later in studying the noise immunity of telephonic communication with pulse modulation.

6-2 Determination of the probability of the transmitted parameter

Let the transmitted parameter λ be a dimensionless quantity which can take on any value from -1 to +1 with the same probability. Clearly, if these conditions are not satisfied, then they can be satisfied by introducing a new parameter and suitably modifying the calculation. We assume that when the parameter which is to be transmitted lies in the range $(k/m) < \lambda < (k+1)/m$, where $k = -m, -m+1, \ldots, 0, \ldots, m-1$, we send instead the parameter $\lambda_k = (k/m)$. In transmission of this type we get errors which do not exceed $1/m$, which is entirely permissible if m is chosen large enough. Obviously, under these conditions, the signal can have the 2m discrete values

$$A(\lambda_k, t) = A_k(t)$$

and we can apply to it the considerations of Chapter 3. Thus, if we assume that the received waveform is X(t), then, according to Eqs. (3-10) and (3-7), the probability that the transmitted parameter has the value λ_k, which means that the transmitted signal was $A_k(t)$, is equal to the quantity

$$P_x(A_k) = \frac{\exp\left[-\frac{T\,\overline{(X(t) - A(\lambda_k, t))^2}}{\sigma^2}\right]}{\sum_{k=-m}^{m-1} \exp\left[-\frac{T\,\overline{(X(t) - A(\ell/m, t))^2}}{\sigma^2}\right]}$$

as follows from the conditions

$$P(A_{-m}) = \cdots = P(A_o) = P(A_1) = \cdots = P(A_{m-1})$$

which are satisfied by the signals under consideration.

It follows from this that the probability that when $X(t)$ is received, the transmitted parameter λ lies in the range

$$\lambda' < \lambda < \lambda''$$

where $\lambda' = k'/m$ and $\lambda'' = k''/m$, is equal to

$$P_x(\lambda' < \lambda < \lambda'') = \frac{\sum_{k=k'}^{k''} \exp\left[- \frac{T\ \overline{(X(t) - A(k/m), t))^2}}{\sigma^2} \right]}{\sum_{k=-m}^{m-1} \exp\left[- \frac{T\ \overline{(X(t) - A(k/m, t))^2}}{\sigma^2} \right]}$$

Now if we multiply the numerator and denominator of this fraction by $\Delta\lambda = 1/m$, and let $1/m$ approach zero, the sums approach integrals, and we obtain

$$P_x(\lambda' < \lambda < \lambda'') = \frac{\int_{\lambda'}^{\lambda''} \exp\left[- \frac{T\ \overline{(X(t) - A(\lambda, t))^2}}{\sigma^2} \right] d\lambda}{\int_{-1}^{+1} \exp\left[- \frac{T\ \overline{(X(t) - A(\lambda, t))^2}}{\sigma^2} \right] d\lambda} \qquad (6\text{-}4)$$

Setting $\lambda'' = \lambda' + d\lambda$, we arrive at the expression

$$P_x(\lambda' < \lambda < \lambda' + d\lambda) = \frac{\exp\left[- \frac{T\ \overline{(X(t) - A(\lambda, t))^2}}{\sigma^2} \right] d\lambda}{\int_{-1}^{+1} \exp\left[- \frac{T\ \overline{(X(t) - A(\lambda, t))^2}}{\sigma^2} \right] d\lambda} = P_x(\lambda')d\lambda$$

or (6-5)

$$P_x(\lambda') = K_x \exp\left[- \frac{T\ \overline{(X(t) - A(\lambda', t))^2}}{\sigma^2} \right] \qquad (6\text{-}6)$$

where K_x is a constant which depends on $X(t)$ but not on λ and t.

It follows from what has been said that if we divide all the values of the transmitted parameter into intervals of the same length $d\lambda$, then to the received waveform $X(t)$ there corresponds most often the value of the transmitted parameter λ which lies in the interval

$$\lambda_{xm} < \lambda < \lambda_{xm} + d\lambda$$

where λ_{xm} is the value of the parameter λ' for which the function $P_x(\lambda')$ is a maximum. We shall call λ_{xm} the most probable value of the transmitted parameter λ. It is clear from Eq. (6-6) that the quantity

$$\overline{(X(t) - A(\lambda, t))^2} \tag{6-7}$$

has its minimum value for $\lambda = \lambda_{xm}$. If this function and its derivative with respect to λ are continuous in λ, then clearly λ_{xm} must satisfy the equation

$$\left\{ \frac{\partial}{\partial \lambda} \overline{(X(t) - A(\lambda, t))^2} \right\}_{\lambda = \lambda_{xm}} = -2\, \overline{(X(t) - A(\lambda_{xm}, t))\, A'_{\lambda}(\lambda_{xm}, t)} = 0 \tag{6-8}$$

where we have written

$$A'_{\lambda}(\lambda_{xm}, t) = \left\{ \frac{\partial}{\partial \lambda} A(\lambda, t) \right\}_{\lambda = \lambda_{xm}} \tag{6-9}$$

The receiver which, depending on the received waveform $X(t)$, always reproduces λ_{xm}, the most probable value of the parameter, i. e., the value which minimizes the expression (6-7), will be called the ideal receiver.

6-3 The function $P_x(\lambda)$ near the most probable value λ_{xm}

We now find the quantity $P_x(\lambda)$ (introduced in Section 6-2) near its maximum, i. e., near the most probable value $\lambda = \lambda_{xm}$. The general form of this function is given by Eq. (6-6). If we assume that λ is near λ_{xm}, we can write

$$A(\lambda, t) = A(\lambda_{xm}, t) + A'(\lambda_{xm}, t)(\lambda - \lambda_{xm}) \tag{6-10}$$

Substituting this expression into Eq. (6-6) and taking into account the relation (6-8), we obtain

$$\begin{aligned} P_x(\lambda) &= K_x \exp\left[\frac{-T\overline{(X(t) - A(\lambda_{xm}, t))^2} - T\overline{A'^2_{\lambda}(\lambda_{xm}, t)}\, (\lambda - \lambda_{xm})^2}{\sigma^2} \right] \\ &= K'_x \exp\left[-\frac{T\overline{A'^2_{\lambda}(\lambda_{xm}, t)}}{\sigma^2} (\lambda - \lambda_{xm})^2 \right] \end{aligned} \tag{6-11}$$

where K'_x is a constant which does not depend on λ. Thus, the function $P_x(\lambda)$ obeys a Gaussian curve in the region where Eq. (6-10) can be considered valid. If the noise intensity σ is sufficiently small, the exponent in Eqs. (6-6) and (6-11) becomes so large in absolute value outside the region of validity of Eq. (6-10) that $P_x(\lambda)$ can be neglected outside of this region. In this case, we can regard the probability function $P_x(\lambda)$ as being given by a Gaussian curve everywhere, and the constant K'_x can be easily calculated from the condition

$$\int_{\infty}^{+\infty} P(\lambda)\, d\lambda = 1 \tag{6-12}$$

Substituting into this equation the value of $P_x(\lambda)$ from Eq. (6-11) and integrating, we find

$$K'_x = \frac{\sqrt{T\, \overline{A'^2_{\lambda}(\lambda_{xm}, t)}}}{\sqrt{\pi}\, \sigma} \tag{6-13}$$

Therefore, for sufficiently small noise intensity, we can assume that

$$P_x(\lambda) = \frac{\sqrt{T\, \overline{A'^2_{\lambda}(\lambda_{xm}, t)}}}{\sqrt{\pi}\, \sigma} \exp\left[- \frac{T\, \overline{A'^2_{\lambda}(\lambda_{xm}, t)}}{\sigma^2} (\lambda - \lambda_{xm})^2 \right] \tag{6-14}$$

It should be mentioned that in this case $P_x(\lambda)$ depends on the received waveform $X(t)$ only to the extent that the quantity λ_{xm} depends on $X(t)$.

In these calculations, we assumed for simplicity that Eq. (6-11) is valid for all values of λ lying between $-\infty$ and $+\infty$. However, this will not always be true, even for small σ. In fact, $P_x(\lambda)$ must always vanish for $\lambda < -1$ and $\lambda > +1$, which means that Eqs. (6-13) and (6-14) can give a big error when λ_{xm} is near ± 1. Therefore, the results obtained in this section and in subsequent sections based on this one, require amplification in the case where λ_{xm} is near ± 1.

6-4 Error and optimum noise immunity in the presence of low intensity noise

Suppose that when the waveform $X(t)$ arrives, the receiver, which is not necessarily ideal, reproduces a parameter λ_x, which is a function of the waveform. We now determine the resulting mean square error. As already remarked in Section 6-2, $P_x(\lambda)\, d\lambda$ is the probability that if $X(t)$ is received, the transmitted parameter lies in the interval $\lambda, \lambda + d\lambda$. This is also the probability that the value of the parameter reproduced by the receiver has an error lying in the interval $\lambda - \lambda_x$, $\lambda + d\lambda - \lambda_x$. Therefore, in this case, the mean square error δ_m is given by the expression

$$\delta_m^2 = \int_{-1}^{+1} (\lambda - \lambda_x)^2 P_x(\lambda)\, d\lambda = \int_{-1}^{+1} \lambda^2 P_x(\lambda)\, d\lambda - 2\lambda_x \int_{-1}^{+1} \lambda P_x(\lambda)\, d\lambda + \lambda_x^2$$

since

$$\int_{-1}^{+1} P_x(\lambda)\, d\lambda = 1.$$

As is evident from this formula, δ_m^2 varies with the choice of λ_x in accordance with a parabolic law, and has a minimum for some value $\lambda = \lambda_{xo}$. Differentiating δ_m^2 with respect to λ_x, and setting this derivative equal to zero, we obtain an equation for λ_{xo} of the form

$$(d(\delta_m^2)/d\lambda_x)_{\lambda_x = \lambda_{xo}} = -2 \int_{-1}^{+1} \lambda P_x(\lambda)\, d\lambda + 2\lambda_{xo} = 0$$

whence

$$\lambda_{xo} = \int_{-1}^{+1} \lambda P_x(\lambda)\, d\lambda \qquad (6\text{-}15)$$

or, what amounts to the same thing, λ_{xo} is the abcissa of the center of mass of the area under the curve $P_x(\lambda)$. We shall call λ_{xo} the optimum value of the parameter λ.

If the waveform X(t) is received, then the minimum value of the mean square error, which is obtained if the receiver reproduces the value λ_{xo}, is given by the expression

$$\delta_{mm}^2 = \int_{-1}^{+1} (\lambda - \lambda_{xo})^2 P_x(\lambda)\, d\lambda \qquad (6\text{-}16)$$

It should be remarked that in the case where $P_x(\lambda)$ is a symmetric curve with a single maximum, then the abcissa of the center of mass of the curve obviously coincides with the abcissa of the maximum, which means that in this case

$$\lambda_{xo} = \lambda_{xm} \qquad (6\text{-}17)$$

Thus, according to the result of the preceding section, we can assert that when the noise is sufficiently weak, in which case $P_x(\lambda)$ obeys a Gaussian distribution (which is symmetric), then λ_{xo} and λ_{xm} are equal, and the ideal receiver gives the least mean square error. Using Eqs. (6-16) and (6-14), we can find that this error is

$$\delta_{mm}^2 = \frac{\sigma^2}{2T\, A_\lambda'^2(\lambda_{xm}, t)} \qquad (6\text{-}18)$$

This is the least possible error for sufficiently small σ. It is obtained with the ideal receiver and obviously determines the optimum noise immunity in the presence of weak noise. Here, and in what follows, we understand weak noise to be noise that has an intensity low enough to make the considerations of Section 6-3 valid. As is evident from Eq. (6-18), the optimum noise immunity for transmission of a parameter is proportional to the specific energy of the waveform $A'_{\lambda}(\lambda_{xm}, t)$, i.e., of the derivative of the signal with respect to the transmitted parameter.

Using Eq. (6-16), we can also determine the mean square error for large noise intensities. However, it is difficult to use this error to evaluate the optimum noise immunity. The point is that for large σ, the character of the function $P_x(\lambda)$ begins to depend on the received signal X(t), and therefore the quantity δ_{mm} given by Eq. (6-16) also depends on X(t). In this case, in order to evaluate the noise immunity, we must also evaluate the probability of the various values of X(t), which leads to a series of mathematical difficulties. In Chapter 8 we shall return to the problem of the evaluation of the optimum noise immunity when the noise intensity is large.

We now find the probability that, in the presence of weak noise, the ideal receiver reproduces the value of the transmitted parameter with an error exceeding ϵ in absolute value. Obviously, this probability is equal to

$$P(|\delta| > \epsilon) = \int_{-1}^{\lambda_{xm} - \epsilon} P_x(\lambda)\, d\lambda + \int_{\lambda_{xm} + \epsilon}^{+1} P_x(\lambda)\, d\lambda$$

Using Eq. (6-14), and keeping in mind the notation used in Eq. (2-47), we obtain

$$P(|\delta| > \epsilon) = 2V\left[\frac{\sqrt{2T\,\overline{A'^2_{\lambda}(\lambda_{xm}, t)}}}{\sigma}\,\epsilon\right] = 2V\left(\frac{\epsilon}{\delta_{mm}}\right) \tag{6-19}$$

6-5 Second method of determining the error and optimum noise immunity in the presence of low intensity noise

There is a second method of finding the size of the error for the case of transmission of a parameter in the presence of low intensity noise. Although this method gives a result which coincides with that already obtained, we shall examine it anyway, since this method is interesting in its own right, and since we shall use it later, albeit in a more complicated form. As before, let the signal $A(\lambda, t)$ represent some transmitted parameter λ. The noise $W_{\mu,\nu}(t)$ may or may not be added to the signal, with the result that a waveform X(t) acts upon the receiver; this waveform is $A(\lambda, t)$ if there is no noise, and $A(\lambda, t) + W_{\mu,\nu}(t)$ in the presence of noise. We represent the waveform by

$$X(t) = \sum_{k=1}^{n} x_k C_k(t) \tag{6-20}$$

where the $C_k(t)$ are given orthonormal functions. Then $X(t)$ is completely characterized by the values $x_1, \ldots, x_n$. Depending on the received waveform $X(t)$, the receiver reproduces some value of the parameter λ, a value which may or may not coincide with the transmitted value. We assume that to each waveform $X(t)$ acting upon the receiver corresponds a specified value of the parameter, which is reproduced by the receiver. Clearly, for every receiver the reproduced parameter equals some function

$$\lambda = F(x_1, x_2, \ldots, x_n) \tag{6-21}$$

which characterizes its operation.

Suppose the received waveform receives an increment

$$dX(t) = \sum_{k=1}^{n} dx_k\, C_k(t) \tag{6-22}$$

Obviously, in this case the parameter value reproduced by the receiver also receives an increment, equal to

$$d\lambda = \sum_{k=1}^{n} \frac{\partial F}{\partial x_k} dx_k = \overline{L(t)\, dX(t)} \tag{6-23}$$

where we have designated

$$L(t) = \sum_{k=1}^{n} \frac{\partial F}{\partial x_k} C_k(t) \tag{6-24}$$

as follows from (2-22). Suppose that the transmitted parameter is changed by $d\lambda$ and suppose that no noise is added to the signal; then the waveform arriving at the receiver changes by an amount

$$dX(t) = A'_\lambda(\lambda, t)\, d\lambda \tag{6-25}$$

where

$$A'_\lambda(\lambda, t) = \frac{\partial A(\lambda, t)}{\partial \lambda} \tag{6-26}$$

We assume that in the case where no noise is added to the signal, the receiver reproduces the transmitted parameter without error. Therefore, in this case the signal that is reproduced must also change by an amount $d\lambda$. According to Eq. (6-23), we obtain

$$d\lambda = \overline{L(t)\, A'_\lambda(\lambda, t)}\, d\lambda$$

Thus, for a receiver which reproduces the transmitted parameter without error in the absence of noise, the relation

$$\overline{L(t)\, A'_\lambda(\lambda, t)} = 1 \tag{6-27}$$

must be valid.

Now suppose that sufficiently weak noise $W_{\mu,\nu}(t)$ is added to the transmitted signal. Then, due to the action of the noise the receiver waveform receives an increment

$$dX(t) = W_{\mu,\nu}(t)$$

so that, according to Eq. (6-23), the parameter which is reproduced receives an increment

$$\delta = d\lambda = L(t)\, W_{\mu,\nu}(t) = \frac{\sigma}{\sqrt{2T}} \sqrt{\overline{L^2(t)}}\ \theta \tag{6-28}$$

The last equality follows from Eq. (2-60). Thus, when the receiver reproduces the parameter value, the error obtained as a result of the addition of noise is a random variable which obeys a Gauss law. As follows from Eq. (2-50), the mean square error is given by the quantity

$$\delta_m^2 = \overline{L^2(t)}\, \frac{\sigma^2}{2T} \tag{6-29}$$

We now find what kind of receiver is needed to make the mean square error a minimum. Clearly, to do this we need to choose the receiver so as to make the quantity $\overline{L^2(t)}$ a minimum, while satisfying the constraint (6-27). It is apparent that any function $L(t)$ can always be represented as a sum of two terms

$$L(t) = L_1(t) + L_2(t) \tag{6-30}$$

where the first term "coincides in direction" with the function $A'_\lambda(\lambda, t)$, i. e.

$$L_1(t) = \rho A'(\lambda, t) \tag{6-31}$$

where ρ is some constant, and the second term is orthogonal to this function, i. e.,

$$\overline{L_2(t)\, A'_\lambda(\lambda, t)} = \left(\frac{1}{\rho}\right) \overline{L_2(t)\, L_1(t)} = 0 \tag{6-32}$$

Then

$$\overline{L(t)\, A'_\lambda(\lambda, t)} = \overline{L_1(t)\, A'_\lambda(\lambda, t)} = \rho\, \overline{A'^2_\lambda(\lambda, t)} \tag{6-33}$$

which according to the condition (6-27) gives

$$\rho = \frac{1}{\overline{A'^2(\lambda, t)}} \tag{6-34}$$

whence

$$L_1(t) = \frac{A'_\lambda(\lambda, t)}{\overline{A'^2_\lambda(\lambda, t)}} \qquad (6\text{-}35)$$

As far as $L_2(t)$ is concerned, it does not enter into the condition (6-27), and can take on any value. Moreover

$$\overline{L^2(t)} = \overline{L_1^2(t)} + \overline{L_2^2(t)}$$

since

$$\overline{L_1(t)\, L_2(t)} = 0$$

It follows from this formula that, under the constraint (6-27), $\overline{L^2(t)}$ has its minimum value for $L_2(t) = 0$. Thus we obtain the minimum value of the error if

$$L(t) \quad \frac{A'_\lambda(\lambda, t)}{\overline{A'^2_\lambda(\lambda, t)}} \qquad (6\text{-}36)$$

so that, according to Eq. (6-28), this minimum error δ_m equals

$$\delta_m = \frac{\sigma}{\sqrt{2T\, \overline{A'^2_\lambda(\lambda, t)}}} \quad \theta \qquad (6\text{-}37)$$

from which we obtain for the minimum value of the mean square error the expression

$$E\,\delta_m^2 = \delta_{mm}^2 = \frac{\sigma^2}{2T\, \overline{A'^2_\lambda(\lambda, t)}} \qquad (6\text{-}38)$$

which coincides with the formula (6-18) previously obtained for this quantity.

6-6 Summary of Chapter 6

The basic results obtained in Chapter 6 can be formulated as follows: Suppose the parameter λ is transmitted using the signal $A(\lambda, t)$, which is a continuous function of λ ; then the smallest mean square error produced by the addition of low intensity noise to the signal is obtained for the ideal receiver, which, when a waveform $X(t)$ is received, reproduces the value of the parameter λ for which the quantity

$$\overline{(X(t) - A(\lambda, t))^2} \qquad (6\text{-}39)$$

has its minimum value. Moreover, when the parameter is reproduced, the probability of getting some value or other of the error obeys a Gauss law, and δ^2_{mm}, the mean square value of the error is

$$\delta^2_{mm} = \frac{\sigma^2}{2T\,\overline{A'^2_\lambda(\lambda,t)}} \qquad (6\text{-}40)$$

where

$$A'_\lambda(\lambda,t) = \frac{\partial A(\lambda,t)}{\partial \lambda} \qquad (6\text{-}41)$$

This error is the least possible, and characterizes the optimum noise immunity for the signal $A(\lambda,t)$ in the presence of low intensity noise. Thus, under these conditions, the optimum noise immunity is completely determined by the specific energy $T\,\overline{A'^2_\lambda(\lambda,t)}$, and the larger this energy, the larger the immunity.

6-7 Geometric interpretation of the material of Chapter 6

As we have already seen, a waveform can be represented by a radius vector, or, what amounts to the same thing, by a point of a multi-dimensional space. The discrete signals which we considered in the second part of this book could be represented by discrete points. The signals which we considered in this chapter can take on a continuous sequence of values, just like the parameter which they characterize. Therefore, the points which characterize the signal lie on a curve. We shall call this curve the signal curve. If a noise waveform is added to the signal waveform, then the resulting waveform is characterized by a new point which most of the time does not fall on the signal curve.

As we have seen, if the waveform $X(t)$ is received, the most probable value of the parameter is the one for which the expression (6-7) is a minimum, i.e., the value corresponding to the point of the signal curve which is nearest to $X(t)$. This is natural, since the shortest noise vectors are the most probable, which means that it is most likely that $X(t)$ was formed by the addition of a noise vector to the nearest point of the signal curve. We saw that the larger the quantity $\overline{A'^2_\lambda(\lambda,t)}$, the smaller the errors produced by the addition of noise. The quantity $[\,\overline{A'^2_\lambda(\lambda,t)}\,]^{1/2}\,d\lambda$ characterizes the length of the element of arc described by the signal point on the signal curve, when the transmitted parameter is increased by $d\lambda$. It is entirely natural that the larger this element of arc, the smaller the probability that such a displacement is produced by the action of noise. Thus, to increase the optimum noise immunity in the presence of weak noise, one should choose a communication system in which the longest possible signal curve is obtained when the parameter is changed from -1 to +1.

CHAPTER 7

THE OPTIMUM NOISE IMMUNITY OF VARIOUS SYSTEMS FOR TRANSMITTING SEPARATE PARAMETER VALUES IN THE PRESENCE OF LOW INTENSITY NOISE

7-1 Amplitude modulation

In this chapter we shall consider the noise immunity of some systems which are used to transmit separate parameter values in the presence of weak noise in the sense of Section 6-3. First we shall investigate some modulation systems separately, and then we shall compare them. We consider first the case of amplitude modulation, where the signal can be written as

$$A(\lambda, t) = (1 + \lambda)\, B(t) \tag{7-1}$$

where $B(t)$ is some waveform or other, and λ is a constant for a given signal and characterizes the value of the transmitted parameter. For this signal we have

$$A'_{\lambda}(\lambda, t) = B(t)$$

so that the minimum mean square error which characterizes the optimum noise immunity is given by the expression

$$\delta^2_{mm} = \frac{\sigma^2}{2T\, \overline{B^2(t)}} \tag{7-2}$$

where

$$4T\, \overline{B^2(t)} = T\, \overline{A^2(1,t)} = Q^2_M \tag{7-3}$$

The quantity Q^2_M is the maximum specific energy of the signal.

Thus, in the case of amplitude modulation, the minimum mean square error which characterizes the optimum noise immunity is determined only by the signal energy and does not depend on the form of the signal. This result becomes quite apparent if we use the geometric interpretation of the type of modulation in question. In fact, for amplitude modulation, the signal curve is a straight line segment, one end of which is at the origin of coordinates. The longer this line, the greater the noise immunity, but at the same time the greater the length of the maximum radius vector of points on the line, and therefore the greater the signal energy corresponding to this radius vector. It is interesting to note that for amplitude modulation, any noise can be regarded as weak in the sense of Section 6-3, since in this case Eq. (6-10) is valid for all λ. In this case, inaccuracy in the calculation of the mean square error comes about only because of the boundary effect mentioned at the end of Section 6-3.

7-2 Linear modulation

The amplitude modulation just discussed is a special case of linear modulation, for which the signal is defined by the expression

$$A(\lambda, t) = \lambda B(t) + B_o(t) \tag{7-4}$$

where $B(t)$ and $B_o(t)$ are any waveforms. It is easy to see that in this case the minimum mean square error is also given by Eq. (7-2). However, with this modulation, it is possible to decrease the maximum specific energy of the signal, without changing the optimum noise immunity. For linear modulation, the signal curve is also a straight line segment, the length of which equals $2\sqrt{\overline{B^2(t)}}$. By properly choosing $B_o(t)$, we may be able to shift the signal curve in such a way as to shorten the maximum radius vectors of the straight line segment, while keeping its length (and therefore the noise immunity) fixed. As is easily surmised, to do this we must take $B_o(t) = 0$. Then the midpoint of our straight line segment will fall at the origin of coordinates, and the maximum specific energy of the signal will have the smallest possible value.

$$Q_M^2 = T\ \overline{B^2(t)} \tag{7-5}$$

so that the minimum mean square error will be expressed in terms of Q_M^2 as

$$\delta^2_{mm} = \frac{\sigma^2}{2Q_M^2} \tag{7-6}$$

Thus, in this case, we obtain a fourfold gain in power as compared with amplitude modulation. However, the realization of this system entails technical difficulties, since in this case, the receiver must respond to the phase of the signal, which changes when λ passes through zero. For the linear system of modulation, just as for amplitude modulation, any noise can be regarded as sufficiently weak.

The application of non-linear modulation, for which the signal curve is not a straight line, allows one to significantly increase the noise immunity for weak noise without increasing the signal energy. The reason for this is that in this case the signal curve can be greatly lengthened by making it twisted, without thereby increasing the maximum distance between the points of the curve and the origin of coordinates, i.e., without increasing the maximum energy of the signal.

7-3 General case of pulse time modulation

We begin our investigation of non-linear modulation systems with the pulse time system. In this system, depending on the value of the transmitted quantity, the envelope of a high-frequency pulse can be shifted in time without changing its shape. For such modulation, the equation of the signal can in general be written as

$$A(\lambda, t) = U_m\left(t - \frac{\tau_o \lambda}{2}\right) \cos(\omega_o t + \phi) \qquad (7\text{-}7)$$

The quantity τ_o appearing here characterizes the maximum displacement of the pulse when λ changes from -1 to +1. The receiver used with this modulation must somehow respond to the time shift of the receiver pulse. Usually with such a communication system, another signal is transmitted in order to establish a time origin at the receiver. However, we shall not be concerned here with these details, and shall assume that the time origin is known at the receiver.

We now find the mean square error when low intensity noise is added to the signal, and when the reception is with an ideal receiver. For this purpose we use Eq. (6-38). For our signal we have

$$A'_\lambda(\lambda, t) = \frac{\partial U_m\left(t - \frac{\tau_o \lambda}{2}\right)}{\partial \lambda} \cos(\omega_o t + \phi) = -\frac{\partial U_m\left(t - \frac{\tau_o \lambda}{2}\right)}{\partial t} \frac{\tau_o}{2} \cos(\omega_o + \phi)$$

whence

$$\overline{A'^2_\lambda(\lambda, t)} = \frac{\tau_o^2}{4} \overline{\left[\frac{\partial U_m\left(t - \frac{\tau_o \lambda}{2}\right)}{\partial t}\right]^2 \cos^2(\omega_o t + \phi)}$$

We shall assume that the square of the term in rectangular brackets which appears in this term does not contain the frequency $2\omega_o$, which is almost always the case, since the envelope $U_m(t)$ does not usually contain high-frequency components. Then, applying Eq. (2-26), we obtain

$$\overline{A'^2_\lambda(\lambda, t)} = \frac{\tau_o^2}{8} \overline{\left[\frac{\partial U_m(t)}{\partial t}\right]^2}$$

since

$$\overline{\left[\frac{\partial U_m\left(t - \frac{\tau_o \lambda}{2}\right)}{\partial t}\right]^2} = \overline{\left[\frac{\partial U_m(t)}{\partial t}\right]^2}$$

and

$$\overline{\cos^2(\omega_o t + \phi)} = \frac{1}{2}$$

It follows that when the ideal receiver is used, the value of the mean square error is given by the expression

$$\delta^2_{mm} = \frac{4\sigma^2}{\tau_o^2 T \overline{\left[\frac{\partial U_m(t)}{\partial t}\right]^2}} \tag{7-8}$$

As is evident from this formula, the error becomes smaller when τ_o or the specific energy of the waveform $\partial U_m(t)/\partial t$ is increased; the latter equals

$$T \overline{\left[\frac{\partial U_m(t)}{\partial t}\right]^2} = \int_{-T/2}^{+T/2} \left[\frac{\partial U_m(t)}{\partial t}\right]^2 dt$$

The error does not depend on the other signal parameters.

7-4 Special case of pulse time modulation (optimum noise immunity)

To obtain concrete results, we consider a special case of pulse time modulation. Let the transmitted signal be

$$A(\lambda, t) = U_m\left(t - \frac{\tau_o\lambda}{2}\right) \cos\omega_o t = U_o \frac{\sin\Omega\left(t - \frac{\tau_o\lambda}{2}\right)}{\Omega\left(t - \frac{\tau_o\lambda}{2}\right)} \cos\omega_o t \tag{7-9}$$

The envelope of this signal is represented by curve 1 in Figure 7-1. It has its maximum value at $t = (\tau_o\lambda)/2$. The spectrum of the signal lies entirely in the band from $(\omega_o - \Omega)/2\pi$ to $(\omega_o + \Omega)/2\pi$.

We now find the minimum mean square error for this case. We have

$$T \overline{\left[\frac{\partial U_m(t)}{\partial t}\right]^2} = U_o^2 \int_{-T/2}^{+T/2} \left[\frac{\partial}{\partial t}\left(\frac{\sin\Omega t}{\Omega t}\right)\right]^2 dt = U_o^2 \int_{-T/2}^{+T/2} \left[\frac{\Omega^2 t\cos\Omega t - \Omega\sin\Omega t}{\Omega^2 t^2}\right]^2 dt$$

Letting the limits of integration go to $\pm\infty$, which can obviously be done, since T can be arbitrarily large, we obtain

$$T \overline{\left[\frac{\partial U_m(t)}{\partial t}\right]^2} = \frac{\pi}{3}\Omega U_o^2 \tag{7-10}$$

whence it follows by Eq. (7-8) that the minimum mean square error equals

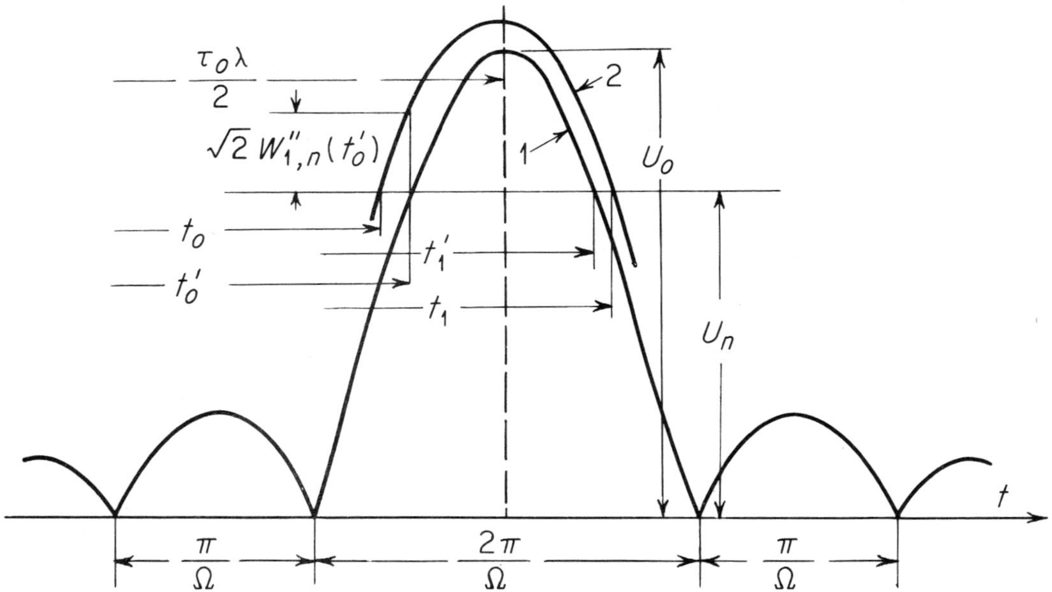

Fig. 7-1. Curve 1 -- envelope of the pulse; curve 2 -- the same with added noise.

$$\delta^2_{mm} = \frac{12\sigma^2}{\pi \tau_o^2 \Omega U_o^2} \tag{7-11}$$

For ease of comparison with other systems, we shall express U_o^2 in terms of the specific signal energy Q. According to Appendix A, the specific energy equals

$$Q^2 = T\, \overline{A^2(\lambda, t)} = \frac{1}{2} T\, \overline{U_m^2(t)}$$

Thus

$$Q^2 = \frac{U_o^2}{2} \int_{-T/2}^{+T/2} \frac{\sin^2 \Omega t}{\Omega^2 t^2}\, dt = \frac{\pi}{2\Omega} U_o^2 \tag{7-12}$$

In this integration, to simplify the result we replaced the limits of integration by $\pm\ \infty$. Introducing this value in Eq. (7-11), we obtain

$$\delta^2_{mm} = \frac{6\sigma^2}{\tau_o^2 \Omega^2 Q^2} \tag{7-13}$$

In this modulation system, all the points of the signal curve have the same distance $\sqrt{\overline{A^2(\lambda, t)}}$ from the origin of coordinates. Hence the curve lies on some hypersphere. As is evident from Eq. (7-13), the noise immunity and therefore the length of the signal curve, increase when τ_o and Ω are increased, while holding constant the specific energy, and consequently the radius of the hypersphere.

7-5 Special case of pulse time modulation (noise immunity for the first method of detection)

As is apparent from Eqs. (7-2), (7-6), and (7-13), the pulse time method of modulation discussed in the preceding section can provide great optimum noise immunity as compared with amplitude and linear modulation. However, for practical purposes, it is important to know how easy it is to realize this large optimum noise immunity. To clarify this question, we examine two concrete methods of receiving the signals considered in the preceding section.

We assume that the receiving apparatus notes the instant of time t_o when the amplitude of the received signal assumes a certain value U_n, e.g., suppose that at this instant a gas discharge tube flashes and that this is recorded on a moving light-sensitive film. Due to the action of noise at the receiver, this instant will be changed and cause an error, which we now find. We assume that there is an ideal filter in the receiver, which passes a band of frequencies from $(\omega_o - \Omega)/2\pi$ to $(\omega_o + \Omega)/2\pi$, i.e., the pass band which contains the components of our signal. Then, obviously, we can consider only the components of the noise which lie in this band. The sum of these components is the process $W_{\mu,\nu}(t)$, given by Eq. (B-6) of Appendix B. Thus, the amplitude of the sum of the signal and noise waveforms can be expressed as

$$U_\Sigma = \sqrt{[U_m(t) + \sqrt{2}\, W''_{1,n}(t)]^2 + 2W'^2_{1,n}(t)} \tag{7-14}$$

If, because of the low intensity of the noise, we take $U^2_m(t) \gg W'^2_{1,n}$, then we can neglect $W'_{1,n}(t)$ and write

$$U_\Sigma = U_m(t) + \sqrt{2}\, W''_{1,n}(t) \tag{7-15}$$

Let us see how much the action of the noise shifts the instant of time recorded by the receiver, i.e., the instant t_o when the value of the amplitude of the received waveforms assumes the value U_n. In Figure 7-1, curve 1 represents the dependence of U_m on t, and curve 2 the dependence of the sum amplitude U_Σ on t. According to Eq. (7-15), the vertical distance between these curves is the quantity $\sqrt{2}\, W''_{1,n}(t)$. It can be seen from the figure how much the time instant t_o is shifted by the action of the noise. This shift gives an error in the determination of λ equal to

$$\delta = \frac{t'_o - t_o}{\tau_o/2} \tag{7-16}$$

since t_o is shifted by $\tau_o/2$ when λ is changed by unity. Here we have denoted by t'_o the instant of time when the amplitude of the signal takes on the value U_n. We assume that the size of the error δ is small enough so that for the time $t'_o - t_o$ the quantity $W''_{1,n}(t)$ can be regarded as constant and the segment of the curve $U_m(t)$ can be regarded as rectilinear. Then the ratio between δ and $W''_{1,n}(t'_o)$ can be found from the figure, and is clearly

$$\left[\frac{\partial U_m(t)}{\partial t}\right]_{t = t'_o} = \frac{\sqrt{2}\, W''_{1,n}(t'_o)}{t'_o - t_o} \tag{7-17}$$

In view of Appendices B and C, we obtain from this

$$\delta = \frac{2(t'_o - t_o)}{\tau_o} = \frac{2\sqrt{\Omega/\pi}\;\sigma\,\theta}{\tau_o\left[\frac{\partial U_m(t)}{\partial t}\right]_{t = t'_o}} \tag{7-18}$$

where θ is a normal random variable. As we see from this formula, as in the case of the ideal receiver, the error δ obeys a Gaussian law. The mean square error equals

$$E\delta^2 = \delta_m^2 = \frac{4\Omega\sigma^2}{\pi\tau_o^2\left[\frac{\partial U_m(t)}{\partial t}\right]^2_{t=t'_o}} \tag{7-19}$$

From Eq. (7-9), we obtain

$$\left[\frac{\partial U_m(t)}{\partial t}\right]_{t=t'_o} = U_o\Omega\frac{x\cos x - \sin x}{x^2} \tag{7-20}$$

where

$$x = \Omega\left(t'_o - \frac{\tau_o\lambda}{2}\right)$$

Giving x various values, we can use Eqs. (7-19) and (7-20) to determine the quantity δ_m^2, which can be written as

$$\delta_m^2 = \frac{12\sigma^2}{\pi\eta_1\tau_o^2\Omega U_o^2} = \frac{6\sigma^2}{\eta_1\tau_o^2\Omega^2 Q^2} \tag{7-21}$$

where η_1 is a function of x, and Q^2 is defined by Eq. (7-12). Using the formula

$$U_n = U_o\frac{\sin x}{x} \tag{7-22}$$

we can find the dependence of x on U_n/U_o, and consequently the dependence of η_1 on U_n/U_o, which is given by the appropriate curve in Figure 7-2. Comparing Eqs. (7-13) and (7-21), we see that since η_1 is always less than one, the noise immunity for the method of reception discussed in this section is less than the optimum noise immunity; moreover η_1 is the efficiency coefficient (introduced in Section 4-2) which shows how much the signal energy (strength) can be reduced with the ideal receiver, while obtaining the same noise immunity, i.e., the same δ_m^2, as with the given means of reception. As can be seen from Figure 7-2, η_1 has its maximum value of 0.58 at $U_n/U_o \approx 0.41$.

7-6 Special case of pulse time modulation (noise immunity for the second method of detection)

We now try to decrease the mean square error as compared with the value we obtained for the first method of detection, described in the preceding section. Such a decrease is possible, since the error obtained was larger than that given by the ideal receiver. To achieve this, we use a receiver which reads not only the instant of time t_o when the amplitude of the received waveform crosses the level U_n from below, but also the instant t_1

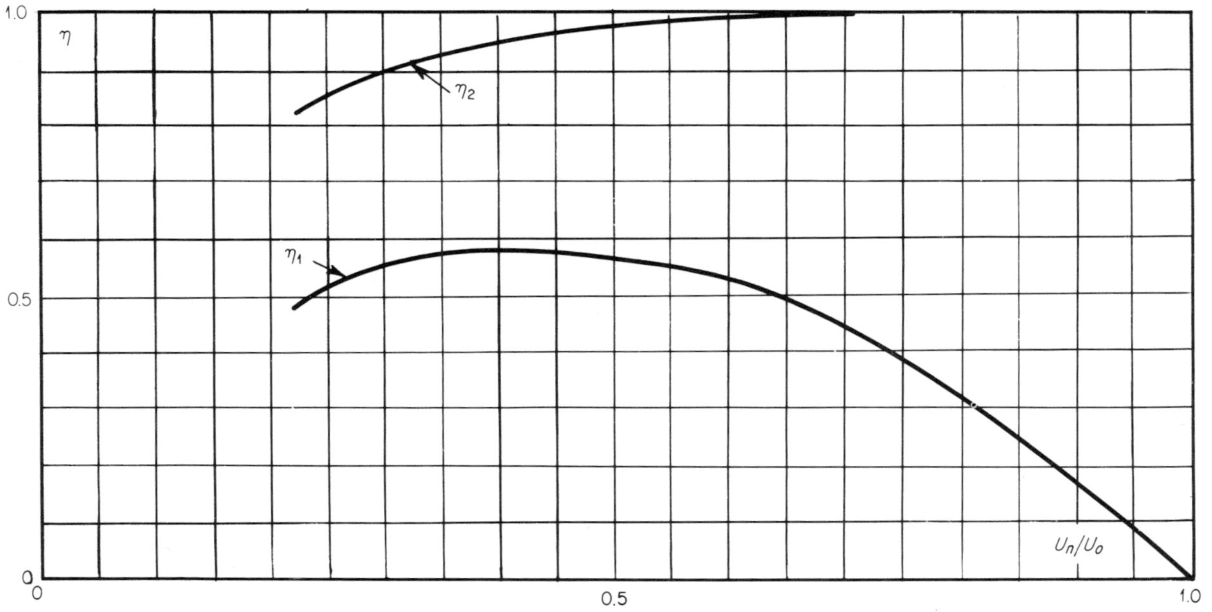

Fig. 7-2. Efficiency coefficient for pulse time modulation; η_1 -- reception with one threshold; η_2 -- reception with two thresholds; U_n -- threshold amplitude; U_o -- maximum pulse amplitude.

when the received waveform crosses the level U_n from above; we take the value of the transmitted parameter to be the mean value

$$\frac{t_o + t_1}{2} \tag{7-23}$$

As a result of the addition of noise, we again obtain an error both in the reading of the instant t_o and in the reading of the instant t_1. We denote these errors by δ_o and δ_1, respectively. Clearly, by Eqs. (7-16) and (7-17) we have

$$\delta_o = \frac{2(t'_o - t_o)}{\tau_o} = \frac{2\sqrt{2}\, W''_{1,n}(t'_o)}{\tau_o \left[\frac{\partial U_m(t)}{\partial t}\right]_{t = t'_o}} \tag{7-24}$$

$$\delta_1 = \frac{2(t'_1 - t_1)}{\tau_o} = \frac{2\sqrt{2}\, W''_{1,n}(t'_1)}{\tau_o \left[\frac{\partial U_m(t)}{\partial t}\right]_{t = t'_1}} \tag{7-25}$$

where t'_o is the instant of time when $U_n(t)$ passes through the value U_m from below, and t'_1 is the instant of time when $U_n(t)$ passes through the value U_m from above. Since $U_m(t)$ is a symmetric function, we have

$$\left[\frac{\partial U_m(t)}{\partial t}\right]_{t = t'_1} = - \left[\frac{\partial U_m(t)}{\partial t}\right]_{t = t'_o} \tag{7-26}$$

Therefore, the error obtained in reading the mean value equals

$$\delta = \frac{\delta_o + \delta_1}{2} = \frac{\sqrt{2}\,[W''_{1,n}(t'_o) - W''_{1,n}(t'_1)]}{\tau_o \left[\frac{\partial U_m(t)}{\partial t}\right]_{t = t'_o}} \tag{7-27}$$

We now find the random variable $W''_{1,n}(t'_o) - W''_{1,n}(t'_1)$. Here we cannot use directly the result of Section 2-5, since the random variables $W''_{1,n}(t'_o)$ and $W''_{1,n}(t'_1)$ are dependent. According to Eqs. (2-54) and (2-74), we can write

$$W''_{1,n}(t'_o) - W''_{1,n}(t'_1) = \frac{\sigma}{\sqrt{2T}} \sum_{\ell=1}^{2n} [I_\ell(t'_o) - I_\ell(t'_1)]\, \theta_\ell$$

$$= \frac{\sigma}{\sqrt{2T}} \sqrt{\sum_{\ell = 1}^{2n} [I_\ell(t'_o) - I_\ell(t'_1)]^2}\; \theta$$

Now we take two terms of this sum and consider Eq. (2-14). We obtain

$$[I_{2i-1}(t'_o) - I_{2i-1}(t'_1)]^2 + [I_{2i}(t'_o) - I_{2i}(t'_1)]^2 = 4\left[1 - \cos \frac{2\pi}{T} i (t'_o - t'_1)\right]$$

whence

$$W''_{1,n}(t'_o) - W''_{1,n}(t'_1) = \sqrt{2}\,\sigma \sqrt{\sum_{i=1}^{n} \left[1 - \cos \frac{2\pi i}{T} (t'_o - t'_1)\right] \frac{1}{T}}\ \theta$$

Bearing in mind that $n = (\Omega/2\pi)T$, letting T approach ∞, and introducing the notation $x = i/T$, $dx = 1/T$, we arrive at the expression

$$W''_{1,n}(t'_o) - W''_{1,n}(t'_1) = \sqrt{2\sigma} \sqrt{\int_o^{\Omega/2\pi} [1 - \cos 2\pi (t'_o - t'_1)x]\, dx}\ \theta$$

$$= \sqrt{2\sigma} \sqrt{\frac{\Omega}{2\pi}\left[1 - \frac{\sin \Omega (t'_o - t'_1)}{\Omega (t'_o - t'_1)}\right]}\ \theta \qquad (7\text{-}28)$$

Substituting this value in (7-27), we obtain

$$\delta = \frac{2\sigma \sqrt{\frac{\Omega}{2\pi}\left[1 - \frac{\sin \Omega (t'_o - t'_1)}{\Omega (t'_o - t'_1)}\right]}\ \theta}{\tau_o \left[\frac{\partial U_m(t)}{\partial t}\right]_{t = t'_o}} \qquad (7\text{-}29)$$

As we see, in this case also the error is a random variable which obeys a Gaussian law.

It follows from the formula just obtained that the mean square error for the given means of reception is equal to

$$\delta_m^2 = \frac{2\Omega \left[1 - \frac{\sin \Omega (t'_o - t'_1)}{\Omega (t'_o - t'_1)}\right] \sigma^2}{\pi \tau_o^2 \left[\frac{\partial U_m(t)}{\partial t}\right]^2_{t = t'_o}} \qquad (7\text{-}30)$$

Giving U_n/U_o various values, and using Eq. (7-2), we can find the quantity $x = \Omega\left(t'_o - \frac{\tau_o \lambda}{2}\right)$, which by the symmetry of $U_m(t)$ equals $\frac{1}{2}\Omega(t'_o - t'_1)$. Then we can use Eqs. (7-20) and (7-30) to find the quantity δ_m^2, obtaining

$$\delta_m^2 = \frac{12\sigma^2}{\pi \eta_2 \tau_o^2 \Omega U_o^2} = \frac{6\sigma^2}{\eta_2 \tau_o^2 \Omega^2 Q^2} \qquad (7\text{-}31)$$

where the quantity η_2, which is a function of the ratio U_n/U_o, is given by curve 2 in Figure 7-2. A comparison of this with Eq. (7-13) shows that η_2 is the efficiency coefficient for the given means of reception. As is evident from Figure 7-2, η_2 is greater than η_1, and is near unity, approaching unity when $U_n/U_o \rightarrow 1$. Thus, this kind of reception is more immune to noise than the kind analyzed in the preceding section, and for all practical purposes achieves the optimum noise immunity. We obtain the optimum noise immunity if $U_n/U_o = 1$, i.e., if we take the readings near the peak of the pulse, or, what amounts to the same thing, if we determine the transmitted parameter by the position of the maximum amplitude of the pulse. It is clear that in the presence of weak noise, one cannot achieve a better means of reception than the one discussed in this section. The reason for the increase of noise immunity is clearly contained in the fact that in most cases (especially when U_n/U_o is near one), the noise which is added to the signal either simultaneously raises or simultaneously lowers both sides of the envelope of the signal pulse, so that the mean value of the quantities t_o and t_1 changes less due to the action of the noise than either of these quantities separately.

7-7 Frequency modulation (general case)

We now consider the noise immunity of a system which transmits continuous values (of parameters) by the use of frequency modulation. In this case the signal can be written as

$$A(\lambda,t) = U_m(t) \cos [(\omega_o + \Omega\lambda)t + \phi_o] \tag{7-32}$$

In order to find the minimum mean square error, we apply to this signal the basic formula (6-40). We find

$$A'_\lambda(\lambda,t) = - U_m(t)\Omega t \sin [(\omega_o + \Omega\lambda)t + \phi_o]$$

and

$$\overline{A'^2_\lambda(\lambda,t)} = \Omega^2 \overline{U_m^2(t)\, t^2 \sin^2[(\omega_o + \Omega\lambda)t + \phi_o]}$$

If we assume that the waveform $U_m^2(t)t^2$ does not contain the frequencies $2(\omega_o + \Omega\lambda)$, then according to Eq. (2-26), we obtain

$$\overline{A'^2_\lambda(\lambda,t)} = \frac{1}{2}\Omega^2 \, \overline{t^2 U_m^2(t)}$$

since we have

$$\overline{\sin^2[(\omega_o + \Omega\lambda)t + \phi_o]} = \frac{1}{2}$$

for sufficiently large T. Substituting this value in Eq. (6-40), we obtain

$$\delta^2_{mm} = \frac{\sigma^2}{\Omega^2 \, T\overline{U^2_m(t)t^2}} \qquad (7\text{-}33)$$

Thus, the larger Ω and the larger the specific energy

$$T\,\overline{U^2_m(t)t^2} = \int_{-T/2}^{+T/2} t^2 U^2_m(t)\,dt \qquad (7\text{-}34)$$

of the waveform $tU_m(t)$, the smaller the error. It is apparent from Eq. (7-34) that this specific energy is proportional to the moment of inertia about the line $t = 0$ of the area under the curve $U^2_m(t)$. According to (A-2), the specific energy of the signal under consideration is

$$Q^2 = T\,\overline{A^2(\lambda, t)} = \frac{1}{2}\int_{-T/2}^{+T/2} U^2_m(t)\,dt \qquad (7\text{-}35)$$

provided that the oscillation $U^2_m(t)$ does not contain the frequencies $2(\omega_o + \Omega\lambda)$, and provided that T is sufficiently large. Thus, this energy is proportional simply to the area under the curve $U^2_m(t)$.

If we wish to increase the optimum noise immunity without increasing the signal energy, we have to increase the moment of inertia about the line $t = 0$ of the area under the curve $U^2_m(t)$ without increasing the area. Clearly, this can be done by increasing the ordinates of the curve in parts which are far from the origin, and decreasing them in parts which are near the origin. By simply time-shifting the envelope of the signal further from the origin, we can also increase the moment of inertia, and therefore the noise immunity, without increasing the signal energy. This last fact may seem strange, but is easily explained. In fact, when $t = 0$, the argument of the cosine in Eq. (7-32), and therefore the expression itself, does not change when λ is changed; the larger t, the greater the change, which must lead to an enhancement of noise immunity. Therefore, shifting the envelope must actually lead to an increase in noise immunity. The significance of this shift can also be explained by the following mathematical transformation. If we time-shift the envelope of the signal (7-32) by an amount t_o, we obtain

$$U_m(t - t_o)\cos[(\omega_o + \Omega\lambda)t + \phi] = U_m(t')\cos[(\omega_o + \Omega\lambda)(t' + t_o) + \phi]$$

$$= U_m(t')\cos[(\omega_o + \Omega\lambda)t' + \omega_o t_o + \Omega\lambda t_o + \phi] \qquad (7\text{-}36)$$

where we denote $t - t_o$ by t'. We see from this last expression that shifting the envelope is equivalent to making the initial phase of the cosine change with λ, which changes the noise immunity as well. We shall consider such a system in Section 7-9.

7-8 Frequency modulation (special case)

In this section we consider the special case of frequency modulation in which the signal is a section of a sine wave of constant amplitude, i. e.

$$A(\lambda, t) = U_o \cos[(\omega_o + \Omega\lambda)t + \phi], \qquad \text{for} \quad -\tau_o/2 \le t \le \tau_o/2$$

$$A(\lambda, t) = 0, \qquad \text{for} \quad t < -\tau_o/2 \quad \text{and} \quad t > \tau_o/2 \tag{7-37}$$

In this case the envelope can be expressed as

$$U_m(t) = U_o, \qquad \text{for} \quad -\tau_o/2 \le t \le \tau_o/2$$

$$U_m(t) = 0, \qquad \text{for} \quad t < -\tau_o/2 \quad \text{and} \quad t > \tau_o/2 \tag{7-38}$$

Therefore, according to the general formulas (7-33) and (7-35), we obtain

$$Q^2 = \frac{U_o^2}{2} \tau_o \tag{7-39}$$

$$\delta^2_{mm} = \frac{12\sigma^2}{\Omega^2 \tau_o^3 U_o^2} = \frac{6\sigma^2}{\Omega^2 \tau_o^2 Q^2} \tag{7-40}$$

Since for frequency modulation, the specific energy of the signal does not change when the transmitted parameter λ is changed, the signal curve lies on a hypershpere, just as for pulse time modulation. Comparing Eqs. (7-13) and (7-40) for pulse time modulation and frequency modulation, we see that the size of the minimum mean square error is given by the same expressions for both kinds of modulation. However, the quantities Ω and τ_o entering into these expressions have a different meaning. In Eq. (7-13), Ω designates half the bandwidth occupied by the signal; in Eq. (7-40), Ω designates half the maximum frequency change of the signal. However, the frequency band required for the transmission of signals by frequency modulation can be regarded as approximately equal to the maximum frequency change of the signal. Therefore, in both formulas, Ω designates half the frequency band needed to transmit the signals. In Eq. (7-13), τ_o designates the maximum time-shift of the signal pulse; in Eq. (7-40), τ_o designates the signal length. However, the time needed to transmit the signal by pulse time modulation can be regarded as approximately equal to the maximum time displacement of the pulse. Therefore, in both formulas, τ_0 designates the time required to transmit the signals. Thus, we obtain the same optimum noise immunity for the transmission of signals by pulse time modulation and frequency modulation, provided that they have the same duration, the same frequency band, and the same energy.

Comparing these two forms of modulation with amplitude modulation (Section 7-1), we see that they afford greater noise immunity in the case where $\tau_0^2 \Omega^2/3 > 1$. The three kinds of modulation considered as examples are far from exhausting the very large variety of possible schemes. We saw that increasing the noise immunity for amplitude modulation required an increase of signal energy. With frequency modulation and pulse time modulation, we were able to increase the noise immunity in the presence of weak noise without increasing the signal energy; rather, it was necessary to increase the time or bandwidth occupied by the signal. In the next section, we shall consider ways of increasing noise immunity in the presence of weak noise which do not require that we either increase the signal energy or that we increase the time or bandwidth occupied by the signal.

7-9 Raising the noise immunity without increasing the energy, length, or bandwidth of the signal

In this section we consider systems where it is possible in theory to increase indefinitely the optimum noise immunity in the presence of noise with sufficiently low intensity, without thereby increasing the energy of the signals or increasing the time or bandwidth occupied by them. Let the transmitted signal be defined by the following expression

$$A(\lambda, t) = U_0 \cos[(\omega_0 + \Omega\lambda)t + \phi + a\lambda], \quad \text{for} \quad -\tau_0/2 \leq t \leq \tau_0/2$$

$$A(\lambda, t) = 0, \quad \text{for} \quad t < -\tau_0/2 \quad \text{and} \quad t > \tau_0/2 \tag{7-41}$$

Thus, this signal differs from the one discussed earlier in connection with frequency modulation in that its phase also changes in accordance with the transmitted parameter. For this signal we obtain

$$A_\lambda'(\lambda, t) = -U_0(\Omega t + a)\sin[(\omega_0 + \Omega\lambda)t + \phi + a\lambda]; \quad \text{for} \quad -\tau_0/2 \leq t \leq \tau_0/2$$

whence

$$T\,\overline{A'^2_{\lambda}(\lambda,t)} = U_o^2 \int_{-\tau_o/2}^{+\tau_o/2} (\Omega t + a)^2 \sin^2[(\omega_o + \Omega\lambda)t + \phi + a\lambda]\, dt$$

$$= U_o^2 \int_{-\tau_o/2}^{+\tau_o/2} \frac{1}{2}(\Omega t + a)^2\, dt - U_o^2 \int_{-\tau_o/2}^{+\tau_o/2} \frac{1}{2}(\Omega t + a)^2 \cos 2[(\omega_o + \Omega\lambda)t + \phi + a\lambda]\, dt$$

The second integral goes to zero as ω_o is increased, and can therefore be neglected for sufficiently large ω_o. Thus we obtain

$$T\,\overline{A'^2_{\lambda}(\lambda,t)} = \frac{U_o^2}{24}(\Omega^2 \tau_o^3 + 12\tau_o a^2)$$

from which it follows that the minimum mean square error characterizing the optimum noise immunity for the signals in question is given by

$$\delta^2_{mm} = \frac{12\sigma^2}{U_o^2(\Omega^2 \tau_o^3 + 12\tau_o a^2)} = \frac{6\sigma^2}{\tau_o^2 \Omega^2 Q^2\left(1 + 12\dfrac{a^2}{\Omega^2 \tau_o^2}\right)} \qquad (7\text{-}42)$$

As can be seen from this formula, the error can be made arbitrarily small by increasing a. At the same time, changing the value of a does not change the energy, bandwidth, or duration of the signal. An analogous result is obtained in the case of pulse time modulation, discussed in Section 7-3, if we change the phase of the high frequency oscillation in proportion to the transmitted parameter.

In practice, it is quite difficult to realize the optimum noise immunity of these systems, since to do so we require a receiver which responds to the initial phase of the high frequency signal oscillation. However, it is possible to propose modulation systems for which it would be easier to realize great noise immunity in practice. An example of such a system with the signal

$$A(\lambda,t) = U_o\,[1 + \cos(\Omega_o t + a\lambda)]\cos(\omega_o + \Omega\lambda)t, \quad \text{for } -\tau_o/2 \le t \le \tau_o/2$$

$$A(\lambda,t) = 0, \qquad \text{for } t < -\tau_o/2 \text{ and } t > \tau_o/2 \qquad (7\text{-}43)$$

This signal has an advantage over the signals considered above in that it undergoes a change in phase of the low frequency oscillation rather than of the high frequency oscillation. This phase is changed less when the signal is propagated, and is more easily detected by the receiver.

The examples considered are far from exhausting all possible versions of modulation systems for which the noise immunity in the presence of weak noise can be made arbitrarily large. For example, such modulation systems can be constructed by the following general principle. Some signal parameter, e. g., a phase, has to change in accordance with the transmitted parameter λ, and an arbitrary change of this signal parameter must not increase the time or frequency space allotted to the signal, nor increase its energy. Thus, this parameter can be changed by an arbitrarily large amount, which thereby makes the signal curve arbitrarily long and arbitrarily increases the noise immunity in the presence of weak noise. However, the variation of this parameter alone is usually not sufficient, since it produces periodic changes in the signal, so that the same signal will correspond to different values of the parameter. To remove this multiple-valuedness, it is necessary to simultaneously vary some other parameter as well, e. g., the frequency of the oscillation, its amplitude, the location of the signal pulse in time, etc. This change must be confined within certain limits, since it usually produces a change in the signal energy, or a change in the time or frequency space allotted to the signal.

The defect of the systems considered in this section is revealed if we study their noise immunity in the presence of noise of high intensity, a topic to which the next chapter is devoted. It is found that the larger we make the noise immunity by the methods presented in this section, the lower the noise intensity at which the boundary between "strong" and "weak" noise occurs, and the formulas which we have derived are not valid for "strong" noise. In the limit, the methods presented here allow one to reduce to zero the error resulting from the action of "weak" noise, but at the same time, "weak" noise comes to mean noise with an intensity which is itself equal to zero. Thus, we cannot succeed in completely nullifying the action of noise by these methods, as might otherwise be expected; we can only obtain a reduction of its effect. This reduction is worthwhile for communication in the presence of noise with sufficiently low intensity, when it is necessary to have very few errors.

CHAPTER 8

NOISE IMMUNITY FOR TRANSMISSION OF SEPARATE PARAMETER VALUES IN THE PRESENCE OF STRONG NOISE

8-1 Derivation of the general formulas for evaluating the effect of high intensity noise

In this chapter we evaluate the optimum noise immunity for transmission of parameters in the presence of high intensity noise. We denote by $P_{\lambda_a}(\lambda > \lambda_b)$ the probability that when the parameter value λ_a is transmitted, the receiver, as a result of the addition of noise to the signal, reproduces a parameter λ satisfying the condition $\lambda > \lambda_b$; by $P_{\lambda_a}(\lambda < \lambda_b)$ we denote the probability that when the parameter value λ_a is transmitted, the receiver, as a result of the addition of noise to the signal, reproduces a parameter value satisfying the condition $\lambda < \lambda_b$. Obviously, these probabilities depend on both the method of transmission, i.e., on $A(\lambda, t)$, and on the method of reception. With this notation, the probability that the error δ exceeds ϵ in absolute value, if the parameter λ_1 was transmitted, equals

$$P_{\lambda_1}(\lambda > \lambda_1 + \epsilon) + P_{\lambda_1}(\lambda < \lambda_1 - \epsilon)$$

We shall assume that the transmitted parameter λ_1 can take on any value in the range -1, +1, with equal probability. Then the probability that λ_1 satisfies the inequality

$$\lambda_2 \leq \lambda_1 \leq \lambda_2 + d\lambda_2$$

and that at the same time $|\delta| > \epsilon$, is equal to

$$[P_{\lambda_2}(\lambda > \lambda_2 + \epsilon) + P_{\lambda_2}(\lambda < \lambda_2 - \epsilon)] \frac{d\lambda_2}{2}$$

Hence, the probability that the error exceeds ϵ in absolute value, when a parameter value λ_1 (not known in advance) is transmitted, equals

$$P(|\delta| > \epsilon) = \int_{-1}^{+1} [P_{\lambda_2}(\lambda > \lambda_2 + \epsilon) + P_{\lambda_2}(\lambda < \lambda_2 - \epsilon)] \frac{d\lambda_2}{2}$$

$$= \int_{-1}^{+1} P_{\lambda_2}(\lambda > \lambda_2 + \epsilon) \frac{d\lambda_2}{2} + \int_{-1}^{+1} P_{\lambda_2}(\lambda < \lambda_2 - \epsilon) \frac{d\lambda_2}{2}$$

Clearly, the value of the integrals is not changed if we substitute the quantity $\lambda_o = \lambda_2 + \epsilon$ into the first integral, and the quantity $\lambda_o = \lambda_2 - \epsilon$ into the second, making corresponding changes in the limits of integration. Then we obtain

$$P(|\delta| > \epsilon) = \int_{-1+\epsilon}^{+1+\epsilon} P_{\lambda_o - \epsilon}(\lambda > \lambda_o) \frac{d\lambda_o}{2} + \int_{-1-\epsilon}^{+1-\epsilon} P_{\lambda_o + \epsilon}(\lambda < \lambda_o) \frac{d\lambda_o}{2}$$

$$\geq \int_{-(1-\epsilon)}^{1-\epsilon} P_{\lambda_o - \epsilon}(\lambda > \lambda_o) + P_{\lambda_o + \epsilon}(\lambda < \lambda_o) \frac{d\lambda_o}{2}$$

since the expressions under the integrals are always positive.

Let us digress a bit to calculate the quantity in rectangular brackets. Let $A_1(t) = A(\lambda_o - \epsilon, t)$ and $A_2(t) = A(\lambda_o + \epsilon, t)$ be two discrete signals, such as were discussed in Chapter 4. Let the receiver under consideration, which serves to determine the parameter λ, be used to receive these signals. We shall say that the first signal $A_1(t) = A(\lambda_o - \epsilon, t)$ was sent if the receiver reproduces a $\lambda < \lambda_o$, and that the second signal was sent if the receiver reproduces a $\lambda > \lambda_o$. Then the probability of error for these signals and the given receiver is

$$\frac{1}{2}\,[P_{\lambda_o - \epsilon}(\lambda > \lambda_o) + P_{\lambda_o + \epsilon}(\lambda < \lambda_o)]$$

is we assume that the a priori probability of transmitting either signal is the same. However, this probability of error cannot be less than the probability of error (given by Eq. (4-8)) which determines the optimum noise immunity for the signals in question, i.e.

$$\frac{1}{2}\,[P_{\lambda_o - \epsilon}(\lambda > \lambda_o) + P_{\lambda_o + \epsilon}(\lambda < \lambda_o)] \geq V(\alpha_1)$$

where $V(\alpha)$ is defined by Eq. (2-47); α_1 is defined by Eq. (4-4) and in this case equals

$$\alpha_1 = \sqrt{\frac{T}{2\sigma^2}\,\overline{[A(\lambda_o + \epsilon, t) - A(\lambda_o - \epsilon, t)]^2}}$$

$$= \sqrt{\frac{1}{2\sigma^2} \int_{-T/2}^{+T/2} [A(\lambda_o + \epsilon, t) - A(\lambda_o - \epsilon, t)]^2\, dt} \qquad (8\text{-}1)$$

From this we obtain the universal formula

$$P(|\delta| > \epsilon) \geq \int_{-(1-\epsilon)}^{1-\epsilon} V(\alpha_1)\, d\lambda_o \qquad (8\text{-}2)$$

for calculating the probability of errors greater than ϵ. In many cases α_1 does not depend on λ_o. If this is the case, the quantity under the integral is constant, and we obtain

$$P(|\delta| > \epsilon) \geq 2(1-\epsilon)\, V(\alpha_1) \tag{8-3}$$

It follows from these equations that the smaller the distance

$$\sqrt{\overline{|A(\lambda_o + \epsilon, t) - A(\lambda_o - \epsilon, t)|^2}}$$

between the points of the signal curve corresponding to parameter values which are separated from one another by the amount 2ϵ, the larger the probability of obtaining an error δ exceeding ϵ.

8-2 Comparison of the formulas for weak and strong noise

We now compare the result obtained in the preceding section with the result obtained in Chapter 6 for the case of weak noise; there we derived Eq. (6-19), which gives the probability that the error δ is greater than ϵ, for the ideal receiver in the presence of weak noise. This formula is valid for a given most probable value λ_{xm}. If we assume that all λ_{xm} are equally probable, then when λ_{xm} is not known in advance, we obtain the following expression for the probability in question:

$$P(|\delta| > \epsilon) = \int_{-1}^{+1} V(\alpha)\, d\lambda_{xm} \tag{8-4}$$

where

$$\alpha = \frac{\sqrt{2T\, \overline{A_\lambda'^2(\lambda_{xm}, t)}}}{\sigma}\, \epsilon \tag{8-5}$$

Let us compare this result with the result given by Eq. (8-2), which is universal and is suitable both for strong and weak noise. For small ϵ, we can take

$$A(\lambda_o + \epsilon, t) - A(\lambda_o - \epsilon, t) = A_\lambda'(\lambda_o, t)\, 2\epsilon$$

Substituting this value in Eq. (8-1), we obtain

$$\alpha_1 = \frac{\sqrt{2T\, \overline{A_\lambda'^2(\lambda_o, t)}}}{\sigma}\, \epsilon \tag{8-6}$$

This quantity is to be substituted in Eq. (8-2), which gives a lower bound for the probability of error. From these formulas, we see that $\alpha = \alpha_1$, which means that the right sides of Eqs. (8-2) and (8-4) differ only by their limits of integration, a difference which goes to zero as $\epsilon \to 0$. It follows from these expressions that if the inequality (8-2) is changed to an equality, then it gives the value of the probability of the small errors produced by the ideal receiver in the presence of weak noise.

8-3 Pulse time modulation

For amplitude and other linear modulation, the formulas obtained in Chapter 7 are valid for noise of arbitrary intensity, and therefore there is no point in investigating these kinds of modulation using the methods of Section 8-1. The situation is different in the case of pulse time modulation. For this kind of modulation, according to Eqs. (2-26), (7-9) and (8-1), we obtain

$$\alpha_1^2 = \frac{TU_0^2}{2\sigma^2} \overline{\left\{ \frac{\sin \Omega \left[t - \frac{\tau_0}{2}(\lambda_0 + \epsilon) \right]}{\Omega \left[t - \frac{\tau_0}{2}(\lambda_0 + \epsilon) \right]} - \frac{\sin \Omega \left[t - \frac{\tau_0}{2}(\lambda_0 - \epsilon) \right]}{\Omega \left[t - \frac{\tau_0}{2}(\lambda_0 - \epsilon) \right]} \right\}^2 \cos^2 \omega_0 t}$$

$$= \frac{U_0^2}{4\sigma^2} \int_{-T/2}^{+T/2} \left\{ \frac{\sin \Omega \left[t - \frac{\tau_0}{2}(\lambda_0 + \epsilon) \right]}{\Omega \left[t - \frac{\tau_0}{2}(\lambda_0 + \epsilon) \right]} - \frac{\sin \Omega \left[t - \frac{\tau_0}{2}(\lambda_0 - \epsilon) \right]}{\Omega \left[t - \frac{\tau_0}{2}(\lambda_0 - \epsilon) \right]} \right\}^2 dt \tag{8-7}$$

Changing the limits of integration in this integral to $-\infty$ and $+\infty$, introducing the value of the specific signal energy Q^2 given by Eq. (7-12), and integrating, we obtain

$$\alpha_1^2 = \frac{\pi U_0^2}{2\sigma^2 \Omega} \left(1 - \frac{\sin \Omega \tau_0 \epsilon}{\Omega \tau_0 \epsilon} \right) = \frac{Q^2}{\sigma^2} \left(1 - \frac{\sin \Omega \tau_0 \epsilon}{\Omega \tau_0 \epsilon} \right) \tag{8-8}$$

As we see, α_1 does not depend on λ_0, which means that we can use Eq. (8-3) to calculate the probability of error.

The curve a, b, c, d, e in Figure 8-1 gives the dependence of the quantity in parentheses in Eq. (8-8) on the parameter $\Omega \tau_0 \epsilon$, which is plotted as the abscissa. This quantity determines α_1 and $2V(\alpha_1)$ for a given value of Q/σ. In the figure there are five scales along the axis of ordinates, from which the value $2V(\alpha_1)$ can be found directly for the values $Q/\sigma = 1, 2, 3, 4, 6$. Since for small ϵ the quantity $P(|\delta| > \epsilon)$ must be larger than $2V(\alpha_1)$, and moreover must be a monotonically decreasing function of ϵ, then for $\epsilon \ll 1$, the curve representing the dependence of $P(|\delta| > \epsilon)$ on ϵ must lie above the

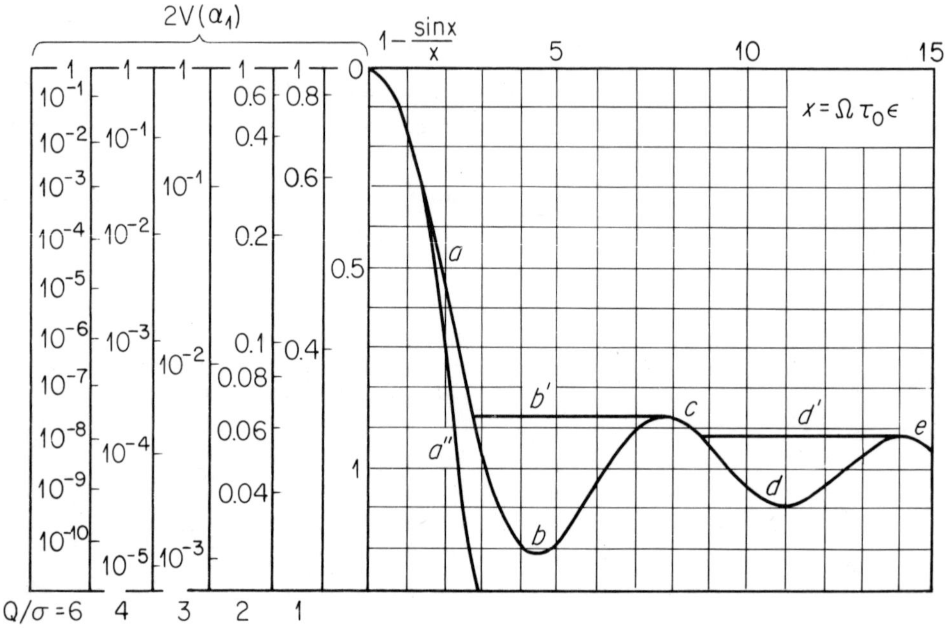

Fig. 8-1. The curve a, b', c, d', e is the lower bound for the probability of an error greater than ϵ for pulse time and frequency modulation and strong noise, for different Q/σ (several scales along ordinate axis); Q^2 is the specific signal energy; Ω/π is the bandwidth and τ_0 the time occupied by the signal; the curve a'' is the probability that the error exceeds ϵ, obtained from the weak noise formula.

curve a, b', c, d', e, obtained from the curve a, b, c, d, e by filling in its valleys. This must be the case for any means of reception, including real reception. Thus, the value of the probability $P(|\delta| > \epsilon)$ which characterizes the ideal receiver must lie above the curve a, b', c, d', e. In the case of weak noise, for small values of the quantity $\Omega\tau_0\epsilon$ and for ideal reception, we can determine $P(|\delta| > \epsilon)$, using Eqs. (6-19) and (8-5). This quantity is represented in Figure 8-1 by the curve a''. It is apparent from an examination of the figure, that for $\Omega\tau_0\epsilon < 2.7$, the curves a, b', c, d', e and a'' are quite close together. However, for $\Omega\tau_0\epsilon > 2.7$, we obtain a drastic divergence between them, with the curve a'' going below the curve a, b', c, d', e, which is impossible, as remarked. It follows from this that for $\Omega\tau_0\epsilon > 2.7$, the formula for weak noise and small errors is completely inapplicable.

We now clarify these results. For the given means of communication and for the methods of reception described in Sections 7-5 and 7-6, small errors are caused by weak noise, which produces a displacement of the sides of the pulse. The probability of this type of error falls off sharply as the error is increased. Large errors are obtained when the noise waveform exceeds the threshold voltage U_n. It is clear that this can happen with almost equal probability at any time. Therefore, the probability of large errors does not fall off much when the error is increased. This property, which is easy to explain for the method of reception in question, is (as shown by Figure 8-1) a necessary feature of the given means of communication, regardless of which means of detection we use. The large errors, for which the formulas derived in Chapter 6 for weak noise are not valid, will be called anomalous. As we see from Figure 8-1, anomalous errors must begin at least from the value $\epsilon = 2.7/\Omega\tau_0$ on. For example, it is clear from the figure that for $Q/\sigma = 2$, the probability that an anomalous error occurs, must be greater than 6×10^{-2}. This means that in more than 6 percent of the cases, on the average, anomalous errors occur for the given value of Q/σ. In general, the probability of occurrence of anomalous errors can be found using the fact that they begin when $\Omega\tau_0\epsilon > 2.7$. Thus, according to (8-8), these errors begin for

$$\alpha^2 = \frac{Q^2}{\sigma^2}\left(1 - \frac{\sin 2.7}{2.7}\right) \sim \frac{Q^2}{\sigma^2}$$

which means that their probability is

$$P(\delta \text{ anomalous}) \geq 2V\left(\frac{Q}{\sigma}\right) \qquad (8\text{-}9)$$

For low intensity noise, the probability of anomalous errors is very small, so that they need not be considered and the weak noise theory can be applied.

8-4 Frequency modulation

We now apply the results obtained in this chapter to the case of frequency modulation, considered in Section 7-8. We have a signal given by Eq. (7-37). Applying Eq. (8-1) to this signal, and taking (2-26) into account, we obtain

$$\alpha_1^2 = \frac{TU_o^2}{2\sigma^2} \overline{\{\cos[(\omega_o + \Omega\lambda_o + \Omega\,\epsilon)t + \phi] - \cos[(\omega_o + \Omega\lambda_o - \Omega\,\epsilon)t + \phi]\}^2}$$

$$= \frac{2TU_o^2}{\sigma^2} \overline{\sin^2\Omega\,\epsilon t \, \sin^2[(\omega_o + \Omega\lambda_o)t + \phi]} = \frac{U_o^2}{\sigma^2} \int_{-\tau_o/2}^{+\tau_o/2} \sin^2\Omega\,\epsilon t \, dt$$

Doing this integral, and introducing the value of the specific signal energy given by Eq. (7-39), we have

$$\alpha_1^2 = \frac{Q^2}{\sigma^2}\left(1 - \frac{\sin\Omega\tau_o\epsilon}{\Omega\tau_o\epsilon}\right) \tag{8-10}$$

Comparing this formula with the formula (8-8) for α_1^2 in the case of pulse time modulation, we see that they are identical. Therefore, all the results obtained for pulse time modulation are applicable to this case also.

8-5 The system for raising the noise immunity without increasing the energy, length or bandwidth of the signal

In this section, we shall evaluate the noise immunity in the presence of strong noise of the system which we discussed in Section 7-9. This system allowed us to make the noise immunity arbitrarily large, provided that the noise was sufficiently weak. In this case, the signal is given by Eq. (7-41), and by a calculation completely analogous to that of the preceding section, we obtain

$$\alpha_1^2 = \frac{Q^2}{\sigma^2}\left(1 - \frac{\sin\Omega\tau_o\epsilon}{\Omega\tau_o\epsilon}\cos 2a\epsilon\right) \tag{8-11}$$

Figure 8-2 shows the curves giving the dependence of the quantity in parentheses in Eq. (8-11) on the value of the parameter $\Omega\tau_o\epsilon$, for three values of a, i.e., $a = 0$ for curve 1, $a = \Omega\tau_o$ for curve 2, and $a = 2\Omega\tau_o$ for curve 3. In accordance with the considerations presented in Section 8-3, the valleys of these curves have been filled in. For a given value of Q/σ, the quantity in parentheses in Eq. (8-11) determines the values of α_1 and $2V(\alpha_1)$. The value of $2V(\alpha_1)$ can be read off at once by using the scales along the axis of ordinates in Figure 8-2.

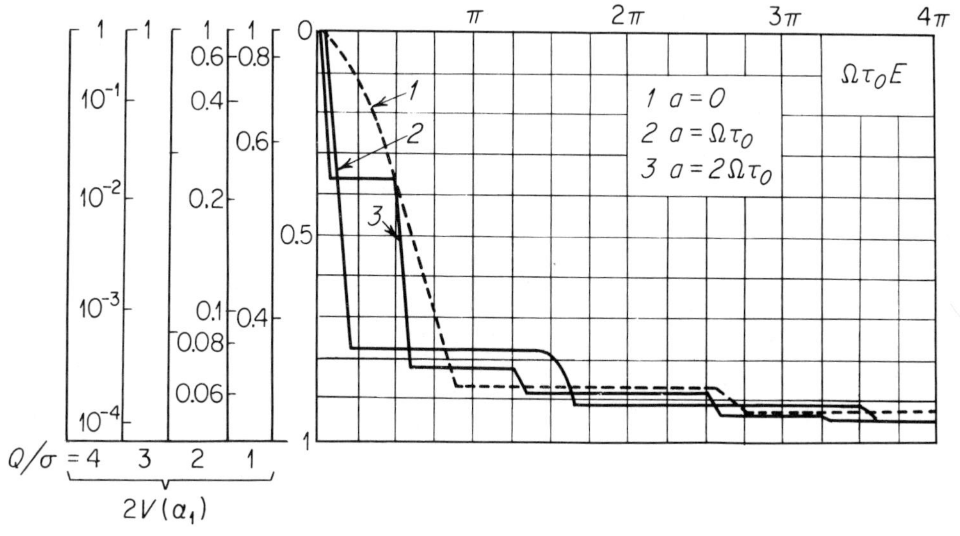

Fig. 8-2. Lower bound for the probability of an error greater than ϵ for the signals given by Eq. (7-41) for various Q/σ. Curve 1 is for $\alpha = 0$, 2 for $\alpha = \Omega\tau_0$, 3 for $\alpha = 2\Omega\tau_0$; Q^2 is the specific energy, τ_0 the duration, and $\pm\Omega/2\pi$ the maximum frequency deviation of the signal.

As we have shown, the probability $P(|\delta| > \epsilon)$ has to be greater than or equal to the value of $2V(\alpha_1)$, if we neglect the effect of the factor $1-\epsilon$ in Eq. (8-3), and moreover equals the value of $2V(\alpha_1)$ for small values of the error ϵ, for weak noise, and for reception with the ideal receiver. It is apparent from the curves shown that the noise immunity for small ϵ, i.e., for small errors, increases as a increases. Thus, under these circumstances, the curves do not restrict the validity of the results obtained in Section 7-9 for this modulation system. On the other hand, it follows from Figure 8-2 that the larger a, the smaller the values of ϵ at which anomalous errors occur, and the larger the probability of such errors. This proves the statement made at the end of Section 7-9 concerning the defects of this and similar modulation systems. However, it is apparent from the curves that if the value of a is not made too large, then the use of such a modulation system can be worthwhile. In fact, comparing the curves of Figure 8-2 for $a = 0$ and $a = \Omega\tau_0$, we see that for small ϵ the value of the quantity in parentheses in Eq. (8-11), and therefore the quantity α_1^2, is ten times larger in the second case than in the first, which greatly increases the noise immunity for weak noise. However, in the second case, anomalous errors begin to occur (as shown by the figure) when the quantity in parentheses has the value 0.78, which is before the value of 2.7 at which they begin to occur in the first case. Therefore, in the second case, the probability of occurrence of anomalous errors is greater than $2V(\sqrt{0.78}\, Q/\sigma)$, while in the first case it is greater than $2V(\sqrt{2.7}\, Q/\sigma)$. If we go to the case $a = 2\Omega\tau_0$, then, for small ϵ, the noise immunity increases further, but at the same time the probability of anomalous errors increases appreciably, and is in this case greater than $2V(\sqrt{0.36}\, Q/\sigma)$.

8-6 Geometric interpretation of the results of Chapter 8

The inequalities (8-2) and (8-3) show that the smaller the distance between the points of the signal curve corresponding to parameter values differing by the amount 2ϵ, the smaller α_1, and the larger the probability that the error exceeds the value ϵ. Thus, the smaller this distance, the smaller the noise immunity. This situation is quite natural, since the smaller the distance between the points corresponding to the two signals, the larger the probability that the signals will be confused for each other and will be incorrectly reproduced by the receiver, as a consequence of the addition of noise and the resulting displacement of the points. For the cases of pulse time modulation and frequency modulation, the value of α_1 and of this distance at first increase in proportion to ϵ, and then stop growing and even begin to decrease from $\Omega\tau_0\epsilon = 4.5$ on (see Fig. 8-1). This property of the modulation allows us to increase the length of the signal curve and thereby increase the noise immunity without increasing the signal energy, but it is also responsible for the appearance of anomalous errors. In geometric terms, the problem of increasing the noise immunity in the presence of weak noise, without increasing the energy, length or bandwidth of the signal, reduces to increasing the length of the signal curve without having the curve leave a certain hypersphere (the radius of which is determined by the maximum energy given to the signal), and without increasing the number of dimensions of the space in question. It is clear that a signal curve of any length can be constructed which lies within the volume of any hypersphere. However, when the length of the curve is increased, the distance between separate "twists" or sections of the curve must decrease, which perforce increases the probability of anomalous errors. Thus, the law which we noted in a special case is obviously valid in general, namely an indefinite increase of the noise immunity in the presence of weak noise without increasing the specific energy, duration, or bandwith of the signal is necessarily accompanied by an increase in the probability of anomalous errors. If we increase the duration or bandwidth of the signal, we thereby increase the number of dimensions of the space in which the signal curve lies. In this case, we can increase the length of the curve without leaving a given hypersphere and without bringing different sections of the curve close together.

PART IV

TRANSMISSION OF WAVEFORMS

CHAPTER 9

GENERAL THEORY OF THE INFLUENCE OF WEAK NOISE ON THE TRANSMISSION OF WAVEFORMS

9-1 General considerations

In communication engineering one deals in many cases not with the transmission of messages which can take on discrete values (as, for example, in the case of telegraphy), nor with the transmission of separate parameter values (as, for example, in the case of the transmission of separate measurements by telemetering), but rather with the transmission of time functions, which can vary continuously and can take on an infinite number of forms (as, for example, in the case of telephony). We shall consider this last type of transmission in Part IV.

To simplify our considerations, we shall assume that the modulating waveform (a sound wave, say) is periodic with period T (this can always be achieved artificially by taking T large enough), and that the frequency spectrum of the waveform contains in effect only components indexed from i_1 to i_2. In this case, we can write the modulating waveform as

$$F(t) = \sum_{i=i_1}^{i_2} (\lambda_{2i-1} \sqrt{2} \sin \frac{2\pi}{T} it + \lambda_{2i} \sqrt{2} \cos \frac{2\pi}{T} it) = \sum_{\ell=\ell_1}^{\ell_2} \lambda_\ell I_\ell(t) \quad (9-1)$$

where the λ_ℓ are certain constants determined by the waveform, the $I_\ell(t)$ are the orthonormal functions defined by Eqs. (2-14), and $\ell_1 = 2i_1 - 1$, $\ell_2 = 2i_2$. For simplicity, we shall assume henceforth that the function $F(t)$ takes values lying between -1 and $+1$, and does not take any values outside this range.

The waveform (9-1) is transmitted by using another waveform, which we shall call the signal (i.e., the modulated waveform). Since we have assumed that the modulating waveform is periodic, we can also assume that the signal is periodic. Inasmuch as the modulating waveform (9-1) is completely determined by $\ell_2 - \ell_1 + 1$ parameters, the signal must depend on these parameters λ_ℓ. Thus, in general, the signal can be represented by the expression

$$A(\lambda_{\ell_1}, \ldots, \lambda_{\ell_2}; t) \quad (9-2)$$

For brevity, we write this expression on occasion as

$$A_F(t) \tag{9-3}$$

The noise $W_{\mu,\nu}(t)$ is added to the signal, so that the received waveform has the form

$$X(t) = A_F(t) + W_{\mu,\nu}(t) \tag{9-4}$$

We assume, as before, that the function $W_{\mu,\nu}$ is periodic, and moreover, that it has the same period T as the period of $A_F(t)$. Clearly, we can always assume this, since in both cases the same requirement is imposed on the period, namely that it be sufficiently large. When the waveform $X(t)$ is received, the receiver has to reproduce $F(t)$ with as great accuracy as possible.

9-2 The influence of weak noise on the modulating waveforms

As we specified, the modulating waveform is completely determined by the parameters $\lambda_{\ell_1}, \ldots, \lambda_{\ell_2}$. Obviously, in reproducing $F(t)$ the receiver thereby reproduces the given parameters. We represent the waveform (9-4) as

$$X(t) = \sum_{k=1}^{n} x_k C_k(t) \tag{9-5}$$

where the $C_k(t)$ are some system of orthonormal functions. Clearly, the parameters reproduced by the receiver are functions of the quantities x_k characterizing the received waveform $X(t)$. Thus we can write

$$\lambda_\ell = \Phi_\ell(x_1, \ldots, x_n), \qquad \ell_1 \leq \ell \leq \ell_2 \tag{9-6}$$

The form of these functions depends on the modulation systems and the receiver. If the received waveform receives an increment

$$dX(t) = \sum_{k=1}^{n} C_k(t)\, dx_k \tag{9-7}$$

then, obviously, the parameters λ_ℓ receive increments

$$d\lambda_\ell = \sum_{k=1}^{n} \frac{\partial \Phi_\ell}{\partial x_k} dx_k = \overline{L_\ell(t)\, dX(t)} \tag{9-8}$$

where

$$L_\ell(t) = \sum_{k=1}^{n} \frac{\partial \Phi_\ell}{\partial x_k} C_k(t) \tag{9-9}$$

We assume that the receiver correctly reproduces the modulating waveform in the absence of noise. Let the transmitted waveform be changed in such a way that λ_ℓ receives an increment $d\lambda_\ell$. Then the signal and therefore the waveform X(t) (since noise is absent) must receive the increment

$$dX(t) = D_\ell(t)\, d\lambda_\ell$$

where

$$D_\ell(t) = \frac{\partial A_F(t)}{\partial \lambda_\ell} \tag{9-10}$$

It follows from (9-8) and the fact that the receiver must reproduce the modulating waveform without error that the relation

$$d\lambda_\ell = \overline{L_\ell(t)\, dX(t)} = \overline{L_\ell(t)\, D_\ell(t)}\, d\lambda$$

is valid, i.e., that

$$\overline{L_\ell(t)\, D_\ell(t)} = 1 \tag{9-11}$$

On the other hand, the remaining parameters λ_i $(i \neq \ell)$ are not changed, so that

$$d\lambda_i = \overline{L_i(t)\, dX(t)} = \overline{L_i(t)\, D_\ell(t)}\, d\lambda_\ell = 0$$

whence

$$L_i(t)\, D_\ell(t) = 0, \qquad i \neq \ell \tag{9-12}$$

Thus, for any receiver which correctly reproduces the modulating waveform in the absence of noise, Eqs. (9-11) and (9-12) must be satisfied, where ℓ is any integer from ℓ_1 to ℓ_2.

Now suppose a modulating waveform is transmitted which is characterized by the parameters λ_ℓ, and let the noise $W_{\mu,\nu}(t)$ (with sufficiently low intensity) be added to the signal which is used to transmit the waveform. Then, due to the action of noise, the received waveform receives an increment

$$dX(t) = W_{\mu,\nu}(t)$$

as a result of which the parameters of the waveform reproduced by the receiver receive increments

$$d\lambda_\ell = \overline{L_\ell(t)\, W_{\mu,\nu}(t)} = \left(\frac{\sigma}{2T}\right) \sqrt{\overline{L_\ell^2(t)}}\ \theta \tag{9-13}$$

and are equal to $\lambda_\ell + d\lambda_\ell$. Thus, the increments $d\lambda_\ell$ resulting from the action of noise are random variables which obey a Gaussian law. The smaller

$$\sqrt{\overline{L_\ell^2(t)}} \tag{9-14}$$

the smaller the increments, and therefore the smaller the errors given by the receiver. If we choose the $L_\ell(t)$ in such a way that they satisfy Eqs. (9-11) and (9-12), and such that at the same time the values (9-14) have the least possible values, then the receiver characterized by such $L_\ell(t)$ will give the least reproduction error for sufficiently weak noise. In the next section, we shall find the optimum values of $L_\ell(t)$; later on, we shall show that the receiver having these values of $L_\ell(t)$ exists, at least in principle.

9-3 Conditions for the ideal receiver

We now find the conditions which the $L_\ell(t)$ must satisfy, i.e., the conditions which the receiver must satisfy, in order that weak noise should produce as small errors as possible in the transmitted waveform. We shall call the receiver which satisfies these conditions ideal. We shall consider the case where all the

$$D_\ell(t) = \frac{\partial A_F(t)}{\partial \lambda_\ell} \tag{9-15a}$$

are mutually orthogonal, and where

$$\overline{D_{2i-1}^2(t)} = \overline{D_i^2(t)} \tag{9-15b}$$

This case is the most interesting, since, as we shall see, these conditions are satisfied for all the modulation systems used in practice. The presence of these conditions will greatly simplify the subsequent considerations and the final results.

Any function, including $L_\ell(t)$, can be written as

$$L_\ell(t) = \frac{D_\ell(t)}{\overline{D_\ell^2(t)}} + B_\ell(t) \tag{9-16}$$

where $B_\ell(t)$ is an as yet unspecified function. Substituting this quantity in Eq. (9-11), we obtain

$$\frac{\overline{D_\ell^2(t)}}{\overline{D_\ell^2(t)}} + \overline{D_\ell(t)\, B_\ell(t)} = 1$$

whence

$$\overline{D_\ell(t)\, B_\ell(t)} = 0$$

Substituting Eq. (9-16) into Eq. (9-12), we obtain

$$\frac{\overline{D_\ell(t)\, D_i(t)}}{\overline{D_i^2(t)}} + \overline{D_\ell(t)\, B_i(t)} = 0$$

However, since $i \neq \ell$, so that $\overline{D_i(t)\, D_\ell(t)} = 0$, we must have

$$\overline{D_\ell(t)\, B_i(t)} = 0$$

Thus, in order for $L_\ell(t)$ to satisfy Eqs. (9-11) and (9-12), it is necessary and sufficient that each $B_i(t)$, $i = \ell_1, \ldots, \ell_2$, be orthogonal to all the $D_\ell(t)$, for $\ell = \ell_1, \ldots, \ell_2$.

According to (9-16) we have

$$\overline{L_\ell^2(t)} = \overline{\left[\frac{D_\ell(t)}{\overline{D_\ell^2(t)}} + B_\ell(t) \right]^2} = \frac{1}{\overline{D_\ell^2(t)}} + \overline{B_\ell^2(t)} \qquad (9\text{-}17)$$

since, as we have explained, $D_\ell(t)$ and $B_\ell(t)$ must be orthogonal. This expression is obviously a minimum for $B_\ell(t) = 0$, whence it follows that for the ideal receiver

$$L_\ell(t) = \frac{D_\ell(t)}{\overline{D_\ell^2(t)}} \qquad (9\text{-}18)$$

where $D_\ell(t)$ is defined by Eq. (9-10).

9-4 Means of realizing the ideal receiver

We now show that the receiver which, when the waveform $X(t)$ is received, reproduces the value of the function which minimizes the expression

$$R = \overline{[X(t) - A_F(t)]^2} \qquad (9\text{-}19)$$

is ideal in the sense formulated in the preceding section. In fact, when a modulating waveform $F_o(t)$ is transmitted in the absence of noise, we obviously have

$$X(t) = A_{F_o}(t)$$

and Eq. (9-19) has its least possible value of zero for the case where $A_F(t)$ and $A_{F_o}(t)$

coincide, and the waveform F(t) reproduced by the receiver is $F_o(t)$. Thus, the receiver in question does not introduce errors in the absence of noise. F(t), and therefore R, is a function of the parameters λ_ℓ. We stipulated that the waveform F(t) reproduced by the receiver is to give the minimum value of the expression R. Therefore, the partial derivatives of R with respect to λ_ℓ must vanish. We obtain the condition

$$\frac{\partial R}{\partial \lambda_\ell} = -2\,\overline{[X(t) - A_F(t) \quad D_\ell(t)]} = 0 \tag{9-20}$$

where

$$D_\ell(t) = \frac{\partial A_F(t)}{\partial \lambda_\ell}$$

If the received waveform receives a small increment $\Delta X(t)$, then, obviously, $A_F(t)$, F(t) and λ_ℓ must also receive increments if the expression for R is again to be a minimum. Suppose the parameters λ_ℓ receive the increments $\Delta\lambda_\ell$; then $A_F(t)$ receives the instrument

$$\Delta A_F(t) = \sum_{\ell=\ell_1}^{\ell_2} D_\ell(t)\,\Delta\lambda_\ell \tag{9-21}$$

which means that we have

$$R = \overline{[X(t) + \Delta X(t) - A_F(t) - \sum_{\ell=\ell_1}^{\ell_2} D_\ell(t)\,\Delta\lambda_\ell]^2} \tag{9-22}$$

The values of the increments $\Delta\lambda_\ell$ must be such that the expression R again has a minimum value. Therefore the partial derivatives of R with respect to $\Delta\lambda_\ell$ must vanish, so that

$$\frac{\partial R}{\partial \Delta\lambda_\ell} = -2\,\overline{[X(t) + \Delta X(t) - A_F(t) - \sum_{\ell=\ell_1}^{\ell_2} D_\ell(t)\Delta\lambda_\ell]\,D_\ell(t)} = 0$$

Moreover, taking into account Eq. (9-20) and the fact that the $D_\ell(t)$ with differenti indices are orthogonal, we obtain

$$\overline{\Delta X(t)\,D_\ell(t)} - \overline{D_\ell^2(t)}\,\Delta\lambda_\ell = 0$$

whence

$$\Delta\lambda_\ell = \frac{\overline{\Delta X(t)\,D_\ell(t)}}{\overline{D_\ell^2(t)}} \tag{9-23}$$

The smaller $\Delta X(t)$ and $\Delta\lambda_\ell$, the more exact Eq. (9-21) is. Letting these quantities go to zero, we arrive at the condition characterized by Eqs. (9-8) and (9-18). Therefore, the receiver which reproduces the waveform $F(t)$ minimizing Eq. (9-19) has no error in the absence of noise, and gives the minimum possible error in the presence of weak noise. Thus, this receiver is ideal in the sense established in Section 9-3.

9-5 The error for ideal reception

We now determine the amount of error given by the ideal receiver when weak fluctuation noise is added to the signal. Suppose a waveform

$$F_o(t) = \sum_{\ell=\ell_1}^{\ell_2} \lambda_{o\ell} I_\ell(t) \tag{9-24}$$

was transmitted. Then, in the absence of noise, the received waveform is $X(t) = A_{F_o}(t)$, and the ideal receiver reproduces the waveform $F_o(t)$ determined by the parameters $\lambda_{o\ell}$. When the weak noise $W_{\mu,\nu}(t)$ is added to the signal, the received waveform is changed by an amount $dX(t) = W_{\mu,\nu}(t)$, and, according to Eqs. (9-8) and (9-18), the parameters λ_ℓ, which characterize the waveform reproduced by the ideal receiver, receive increments

$$d\lambda_\ell = \frac{\overline{D_\ell(t)\, dX(t)}}{\overline{D_\ell^2(t)}} = \frac{\overline{D_\ell(t)\, W_{\mu,\nu}(t)}}{\overline{D_\ell^2(t)}} = \frac{\sigma\,\theta_\ell}{\sqrt{2T\,\overline{D_\ell^2(t)}}} \tag{9-25}$$

It should be noted that the random variables θ_ℓ with different indices are independent, since the $D_\ell(t)$ with different indices are orthogonal. Thus, the waveform reproduced by the ideal receiver has the form

$$F(t) = \sum_{\ell=\ell_1}^{\ell_2} (\lambda_{o\ell} + d\lambda_\ell)\, I_\ell(t) = F_o(t) + \sum_{\ell=\ell_1}^{\ell_2} \frac{\sigma\,\theta_\ell\, I_\ell(t)}{\sqrt{2T\,\overline{D^2(t)}}}$$

$$= F_o(t) + W^*(t) \tag{9-26}$$

where

$$W^*(t) = \sum_{i=i_1}^{i_2} \frac{\sigma}{\sqrt{T\,\overline{D_{2i}^2(t)}}} \left(\theta_{2i-1} \sin\frac{2\pi}{T} it + \theta_{2i} \cos\frac{2\pi}{T} it\right)$$

Comparing this expression with Eq. (D-3), we see that due to the action of the noise which is added to the signal the receiver adds to the modulating waveform $F_o(t)$ normal fluctuation noise with an intensity at frequency i/T equal to

$$\sigma^*\left(\frac{i}{T}\right) = \frac{\sigma}{\sqrt{\overline{D^2_{2i-1}(t)}}} = \frac{\sigma}{\sqrt{\overline{D^2_{2i}(t)}}} \qquad (9\text{-}27)$$

where

$$D_\ell(t) = \frac{\partial A_F(t)}{\partial \lambda_\ell}$$

We shall henceforth call this normal fluctuation noise <u>the noise at the receiver output.</u> This intensity of the noise at the receiver output is <u>the minimum possible and characterizes the optimum noise immunity for a given modulation system.</u> In the case where $\sigma^*(i/T)$ does not depend on i, we omit this index and write σ^*.

9-6 Brief summary of Chapter 9

We call ideal the receiver which exactly reproduces the modulating waveform in the absence of noise, and gives the best approximation to the modulating waveform in the presence of weak noise. The ideal receiver reproduces the waveform $F(t)$ which minimizes the quantity R given by (9-19). When reception is with the ideal receiver and the noise is weak, the reproduced waveform differs from the modulating waveform by the fluctuation noise with intensity given by Eq. (9-27). In drawing these conclusions, it was assumed that the functions $D_\ell(t) = \partial A_F(t)/\partial\lambda_\ell$ are orthogonal for any pair of different indices, and that $\overline{D^2_{2i-1}(t)} = \overline{D^2_{2i}(t)}$.

CHAPTER 10

DIRECT MODULATION SYSTEMS

10-1 Definition

By direct modulation systems we shall understand systems in which the modulating waveform (message) $F(t)$ enters directly as a parameter into the expression for the transmitted signal. In this case, we can write the general form of the signal as

$$A_F(t) = A\,[F(t),\ t\,] \tag{10-1}$$

Examples of direct modulation systems are amplitude modulation, where the signal can be written as

$$A_F(t) = U_o\,[\,1 + MF(t)\,]\ \cos(\omega_o t + \phi_o)$$

phase modulation, where the signal can be written as

$$A_F(t) = U_o\ \cos\,[\omega_o t + mF(t) + \phi_o\,]$$

etc. Frequency modulation, where the transmitted signal is written as

$$A_F(t) = U_o\ \cos\,[\,\omega_o t + \Omega \int F(t)\ dt]$$

does not belong to the direct systems in the sense of the terminology of this book. Since the modulating waveform $F(t)$ appears behind the integral, we shall call this kind of modulation integral modulation. Single sideband transmission is also not a direct system, since in this case also the signal cannot be expressed analytically in terms of the modulating waveform $F(t)$. In Chapter 11 we shall study pulse modulation systems, which are also not classified as direct systems.

10-2 Derivation of basic formulas

Since by hypothesis the modulating waveform $F(t)$ can be expressed by Eq. (9-1), for a direct modulation system we can write the signal as

$$A_F(t) = A\,[F(t),\ t\,] = A\left[\ \sum_{\ell=\ell_1}^{\ell_2} \lambda_\ell I_\ell(t),\ t\right]$$

whence

$$D_{\ell}(t) = \frac{\partial A_F(t)}{\partial \lambda_{\ell}} = \frac{\partial A_F(t)}{\partial F} I_{\ell}(t)$$

We also assume that the function $[\partial A_F(t)/\partial F]^2$ contains only sinusoidal components with frequencies greater than ℓ_2/T, i.e., greater than twice the maximum frequency of the sinusoidal components of the modulating waveform F(t); this condition is usually satisfied. Then, according to Eq. (2-26), we obtain

$$\overline{D_{\ell}^2(t)} = \overline{[\partial A_F(t)/\partial F]^2 I_{\ell}^2(t)} = \overline{[\partial A_F(t)/\partial F]^2}$$

$$\overline{D_{\ell}(t)\, D_k(t)} = \overline{[\partial A_F(t)/\partial F]^2 I_{\ell}(t)\, I_k(t)} = 0 \qquad (10\text{-}2)$$

It follows from these equations that the conditions (9-15) which were imposed on the $D_{\ell}(t)$ are satisfied in this case, and we can use Eqs. (9-26) and (9-27). It is a consequence of these equations that, for the kind of modulation system in question, we have at the output of the ideal receiver not only the modulating waveform F(t), but also normal fluctuation noise added to it. This noise has a uniform spectrum and an intensity which, according to Eq. (10-2), is equal to

$$\sigma^* = \frac{\sigma}{\sqrt{\overline{[\partial A_F(t)/\partial F]^2}}} \qquad (10\text{-}3)$$

It is all right to assume that the noise has the same frequencies as those contained in the waveform F(t), since any other frequencies can be filtered out of the receiver output.

10-3 Optimum noise immunity for amplitude and linear modulation

In amplitude modulation the signal can be represented by the expression

$$A_F(t) = U_o\, [1 + MF(t)]\, \cos(\omega_o t + \phi_o) \qquad (10\text{-}4)$$

where M is the coefficient of modulation, since we agreed to assume that $-1 \le F(t) \le +1$. It follows from this formula that

$$\frac{\partial A_F}{\partial F} = U_o M \cos(\omega_o t + \phi) \qquad (10\text{-}5)$$

This is a high-frequency waveform with frequency $\omega_o/2\pi$, so that the restriction imposed in Section 10-2 is satisfied. Moreover

$$\overline{[\partial A_F(t)/\partial F]^2} = \frac{1}{2} U_o^2 M^2$$

so that, as a result of noise, at the output of the ideal receiver we have normal fluctuation noise with intensity

$$\sigma^* = \sqrt{2}\,\sigma / U_o M \tag{10-6}$$

Here, and in what follows, it is assumed that the gain of the receiver is adjusted so that the waveform produced at its output by the signal is $F(t)$. For convenience in comparing this with other methods of modulation, we express U_o in Eq. (10-6) in terms of the effective value of the signal voltage taken for the cases $F(t) = 0$ and $F(t) = \cos \Omega t$. For $F(t) = 0$, we obtain

$$U_{eo}^2 = \overline{A^2(0,t)} = \frac{1}{2} U_o^2$$

and for $F(t) = \cos \Omega t$, we obtain

$$U_{em}^2 = \overline{A^2(\cos \Omega t, t)} = \frac{1}{2} U_o^2 \left(1 + \frac{1}{2} M^2\right)$$

whence

$$\sigma^{*2} = \frac{\sigma^2}{M^2 U_{eo}^2} = \frac{\left(1 + \frac{M^2}{2}\right)\sigma^2}{M^2 U_{em}^2} \tag{10-7}$$

The maximum noise immunity is obtained for $M = 1$. In this case

$$\sigma^{*2} = \frac{\sigma^2}{U_{eo}^2} = \frac{3\sigma^2}{2U_{em}^2} \tag{10-8}$$

For linear modulation, the signal can be written as

$$A_F(t) = U_1 \cos(\omega_o t + \phi_1) + U_o M F(t) \cos(\omega_o t + \phi_o) \tag{10-9}$$

The amplitude modulation analyzed above, the so called quadrature modulation, and also suppressed carrier transmission using both sidebands are special cases of linear modulation. It is easy to see that Eq. (10-5) is also valid for this kind of modulation, which means that in this case at the output of the ideal receiver, in addition to the modulating waveform $F(t)$, there is normal fluctuation noise, with intensity given by Eq. (10-6).

10-4 Optimum noise immunity for phase modulation

For phase modulation, the signal can be written as

$$A_F(t) = U_o \cos [\omega_o t + mF(t)] \qquad (10\text{-}10)$$

where m is the modulation index. For such a signal, we obtain

$$\frac{\partial A_F(t)}{\partial F} = - U_o m \sin[\omega_o t + mF(t)]$$

whence

$$\left[\frac{\partial A_F(t)}{\partial F}\right]^2 = \frac{U_o^2 m^2}{2} - \frac{U_o^2 m^2}{2} \cos [2\omega_o t + 2mF(t)]$$

In the case where ω_o is large enough, this waveform has no low-frequency components, so that the condition (10-2) is satisfied. Moreover, we have

$$\overline{[\partial A_F(t)/\partial F]^2} = \frac{U_o^2 m^2}{2}$$

which means that, due to the noise, at the output of the ideal receiver we have, in addition to the modulating waveform F(t), normal fluctuation noise with intensity

$$\sigma^* = \sqrt{2}\, \sigma / U_o m \qquad (10\text{-}11)$$

For phase modulation, the effective value of the signal equals

$$U_e^2 = A^2(0,t) = A^2(\cos \Omega t, t) = \frac{1}{2} U_o^2$$

Introducing these values into Eq. (10-11), we obtain

$$\sigma^* = \sigma / mU_e \qquad (10\text{-}12)$$

We see that for phase modulation, the optimum noise immunity is as many times greater than the optimum noise immunity for amplitude modulation as m is greater than M. Since for amplitude modulation M cannot be larger than unity, whereas for phase modulation m can be much greater than unity, we can obtain greater optimum noise immunity for phase modulation than for amplitude modulation.

10-5 Noise immunity for amplitude modulation and ordinary reception

We now compare the optimum noise immunity for amplitude modulation (obtained in Section 10-3) with the noise immunity obtained for this kind of transmission when using an ordinary receiver. If before the detector there is a filter which passes the signal frequencies, then at the filter output the noise voltage has the form given by Eq. (B-6), so that the sum voltage acting on the detector equals

$$U_o [1 + MF(t)] \cos \omega_o t + \sqrt{2}\, W''_{1,n}(t) \cos \omega_o t + \sqrt{2}\, W'_{1,n}(t) \sin \omega_o t \tag{10-13}$$

The amplitude of this waveform equals

$$U_m = \sqrt{\{U_o [1 + MF(t)] + \sqrt{2}\, W''_{1,n}(t)\}^2 + W'^2_{1,n}(t)} \tag{10-14}$$

If the noise is sufficiently small compared with the signal, then quantity $W'^2_{1,n}$ can be neglected compared with the square of the term in curly brackets. Then we obtain

$$U_m = U_o [1 + MF(t)] + \sqrt{2}\, W''_{1,n}(t) \tag{10-15}$$

If we assume that a linear detector is used at the receiver, then the a.c. component at the detector output is equal to

$$K [U_o MF(t) + \sqrt{2}\, W''_{1,n}(t)] \tag{10-16}$$

If at the receiver we use a synchronous detector, which responds only to the cosine component of the voltage (10-13) applied to the detector, then this result is exact even for large noise intensity. If the gain of the receiver is chosen so that the waveform at its output is equal to F(t) in the absence of noise, then in the presence of noise, according to Eq. (10-16), the waveform is

$$F(t) + \frac{\sqrt{2}}{MU_o} W''_{1,n}(t) \tag{10-17}$$

Since, as shown in Appendix B, $W''_{1,n}(t)$ is normal fluctuation noise with intensity σ, then at the receiver output there is added to the transmitted waveform the normal fluctuation noise with intensity

$$\sigma^* = \sqrt{2}\, \sigma / MU_o \tag{10-18}$$

Thus, we see by comparing Eqs. (10-6) and (10-18) that the influence of noise is the same for the real receiver and for the ideal receiver. We can conclude from this that <u>for amplitude modulation, the ordinary receiver with a linear detector provides the optimum noise immunity in the presence of weak noise.</u> Hence, in the case of signals of the form (10-4) and for weak noise, no improvements can give a noise immunity higher than that given by the ordinary receiver with a linear detector.

The same result is also obtained when we investigate other linear modulation systems, e.g., quadrature modulation and two-sideband, suppressed carrier transmission. In these cases it also turns out that the reception normally used with these methods provides the optimum noise immunity.

10-6 Noise immunity for phase modulation and ordinary reception

For phase modulation with the signal given by Eq. (10-10), taking into account added noise, we obtain in the receiver (after the r.f. or i.f. filter) the waveform

$$U_o \cos [\omega_o t + mF(t)] + \sqrt{2}\, W''_{1,n}(t) \cos \omega_o t + \sqrt{2}\, W'_{1,n}(t) \sin \omega_o t \qquad (10\text{-}19)$$

as follows from Appendix B. To simplify the calculation, we consider only the case where the modulating waveform is small and $mF(t) \ll 1$. In this case, for weak noise, when we can take $W''_{1,n}(t) \ll U_o$ and $W'_{1,n}(t) \ll U_o$, we can represent the sum of the waveforms (10-19) by one waveform

$$U_m \cos [\omega_o t + \phi(t)]$$

where

$$\phi(t) = mF(t) - \frac{\sqrt{2}}{U_o} W'_{1,n}(t)$$

If this waveform is applied to a phase detector which reacts only to its phase and not to its amplitude, then after the phase detector we obtain the waveform

$$F(t) + \frac{\sqrt{2}}{mU_o} W'_{1,n}(t)$$

after choosing the gain in the required way. Since, as shown in Appendix B, $W'_{1,n}(t)$ is normal fluctuation noise with intensity σ, then in this case, after the phase detector there is added to the transmitted waveform $F(t)$ the normal fluctuation noise with intensity

$$\sqrt{2}\,\sigma / mU_o \qquad (10\text{-}20)$$

Thus, we see by comparing Eqs. (10-11) and (10-20) that the method of reception examined here provides the optimum noise immunity in the presence of weak noise, at least for small modulation indices.

10-7 Noise immunity for single-sideband transmission

In this section we study the noise immunity for single-sideband transmission. This transmission system does not belong to the direct systems, but is discussed here for convenience. We now find the influence of noise for this kind of transmission and reception with the ideal receiver. If the modulating waveform

$$F(t) = \sum_{i=i_1}^{i_2} (\lambda_{2i-1} \sqrt{2} \sin \frac{2\pi}{T} it + \lambda_{2i} \sqrt{2} \cos \frac{2\pi}{T} it)$$

is transmitted, then if the upper sideband is used, the signal has the appearance

$$A_F(t) = U_o \sum_{i=i_1}^{i_2} \left[\lambda_{2i-1} \sqrt{2} \sin(\frac{2\pi}{T} i + \omega_o)t + \lambda_{2i} \sqrt{2} \cos(\frac{2\pi}{T} i + \omega_o)t\right] \qquad (10\text{-}21)$$

where $\omega_o/2\pi$ is the carrier frequency. From this we obtain

$$D_{2i-1}(t) = U_o \sqrt{2} \sin(\frac{2\pi}{T} i + \omega_o)t$$

$$D_{2i}(t) = U_o \sqrt{2} \cos(\frac{2\pi}{T} i + \omega_o)t$$

Therefore

$$\overline{D^2_{2i-1}(t)} = \overline{D^2_{2i}(t)} = U_o^2$$

and

$$\overline{D_i(t)\, D_j(t)} = 0, \qquad i \neq j$$

Thus, the general formula (9-27) is applicable to the system in question, so that the noise intensity at the output of the ideal receiver equals

$$\sigma^* = \sigma / \sqrt{\overline{D^2_{\ell}(t)}} = \sigma / U_o^2 \qquad (10\text{-}22)$$

We obtain the same noise immunity for reception on the receiver usually used to receive single-sideband transmission.

CHAPTER 11

PULSE MODULATION SYSTEMS

11-1 Definition

By pulse modulation systems we shall understand systems in which, instead of continuously transmitting a modulating waveform $F(t)$ using the signal $A_F(t)$, we transmit only the separate instantaneous waveform values

$$\ldots,\ F(-2\tau),\ F(-\tau),\ F(0),\ F(\tau),\ F(2\tau),\ \ldots \tag{11-1}$$

taken at instants of time separated from one another by the amount τ. We achieve the transmission of these instantaneous values by using separate signals (pulses) which follow one another in sequence. In doing this, we can use any of the methods of transmitting separate parameter values discussed in Part III. In this case, the transmitted (i. e., modulating) quantities are the instantaneous values (11-1).

To transmit the instantaneous value $F(0)$, we use a signal $A(\mu_o, t)$ beginning at $t = 0$, where we have set $\mu_o = F(0)$. To transmit the instantaneous value $F(k\tau)$, we use a similar signal $A(\mu_k, t - \tau k)$ beginning at $t = \tau k$, where

$$\mu_k = F(k\tau) \tag{11-2}$$

Thus, we achieve the transmission of the waveform $F(t)$ by using a signal

$$A_F(t) = \sum_{k=-T/2\tau}^{(T/2\tau)-1} A(\mu_k,\ t - \tau k) \tag{11-3}$$

The choice of the limits in this sum results from the fact that all processes studied in this book have to lie in the interval $(-T/2, +T/2)$. We assume that T is chosen in such a way as to make $T/2\tau$ an integer.

11-2 A way of realizing the pulse modulation system

We now examine a possible way of realizing the pulse communication system, and explain the basic relation which makes the system realizable. The means of obtaining the signal pulses in the transmitter is in principle very simple, and can be schematically achieved as follows: At instants of time which are multiples of τ, a switch closes a circuit on which there acts an e. m. f. proportional to $F(t)$. Then current pulses with values proportional to the instantaneous values (11-1) flow in this circuit. These current pulses act on a modulator, and change the form of the r. f. pulses sent to the receiver by any of the methods studied in Part III. When the r. f. pulses arrive at the receiver, the instantaneous values (11-1) sent by the transmitter are first restored, and then short pulses proportional to these instantaneous values are produced. These short pulses can be written as

$$F(k\tau)\ \Phi(t - k\tau)$$

The voltage produced by all these pulses is

$$\sum_{k=-T/2\tau}^{(T/2\tau)-1} F(k\tau)\ \Phi(t - k\tau) \tag{11-4}$$

Here we do not take into consideration a possible constant delay of the pulses at the receiver with respect to the pulses at the transmitter.

We assume that $F(t)$ is a continuous function and that $\Phi(t) = 0$ for $t < 0$ and $t > +\epsilon$. Then the equation

$$F(k\tau)\ \Phi(t - k\tau) = F(t)\ \Phi(t - k\tau)$$

is valid with arbitrarily great accuracy, if ϵ is sufficiently small. In fact, $\Phi(t - k\tau)$ is different from zero only for values of t which lie in an arbitrarily small interval $(k\tau, k\tau + \epsilon)$ in which we can assume that $F(t) = F(k\tau)$. Taking account of this fact, we can write Eq. (11-4) as

$$\sum_{k=-T/2\tau}^{(T/2\tau)-1} F(k\tau)\ \Phi(t - k\tau) = F(t) \sum_{k=-T/2\tau}^{(T/2\tau)-1} (t - k\tau) \tag{11-5}$$

$$= F(t)\ d_o + F(t)\ d_1 \cos(\omega_o t + \phi_1) + F(t)\ d_2 \cos(2\omega_o t + \phi_2) + \cdots$$

where $\omega_o = 2\pi/\tau$, and $d_o, d_1, d_2, \ldots$ are certain constants. The last expression is obtained by expanding the sum

$$\sum_{k=-T/2\tau}^{(T/2\tau)-1} \Phi(t - k\tau) \tag{11-6}$$

which is a periodic function of τ, as a Fourier series. Let the highest frequency entering the waveform $F(t)$ be f_{max}. Obviously, the highest frequency entering into the first term of the series is equal to this quantity. The second term of the series is an amplitude modulated waveform and can be decomposed into sinusoidal components consisting of the carrier and sidebands, where the lowest frequency of a component is obviously $(\omega_o/2\pi) - f_{max}$. In the third term, the lowest frequency is obviously $(2\omega_o/2\pi) - f_{max}$, and so forth. Suppose that the highest frequency f_{max} of the first term is less than the lowest frequency of the remaining terms, i.e.

$$f_{max} < (\omega_o/2\pi) - f_{max} \tag{11-7}$$

or

$$\left(\frac{1}{\tau}\right) = \left(\frac{\omega_o}{2\pi}\right) > 2f_{max} \qquad (11\text{-}8)$$

or

$$\tau < \left(\frac{1}{2f_{max}}\right) \qquad (11\text{-}9)$$

Then, because of the frequency separation, it is clear that the first term of (11-5) can be completely filtered out from the other components, so that we can obtain F(t). Thus, using the method described, i.e., the pulse representation (11-4) with a filter or harmonic analysis, we can reproduce the waveform F(t), if only the frequency of the pulses is greater than twice the maximum frequency entering into the waveform F(t), or, what amounts to the same thing, if the distance τ between the pulses is less than half the smallest period of a sinusoidal component of F(t).

11-3. Optimum noise immunity for the pulse modulation system

We now determine the optimum noise immunity of the pulse modulation system, starting from Eq. (11-3) and the general formula (9-27). We obtain

$$D_\ell(t) = \frac{\partial A_F(t)}{\partial \lambda_\ell} \sum_{k=-T/2\tau}^{(T/2\tau)-1} \frac{\partial A(\mu_k, t - \tau k)}{\partial \mu_k} \frac{\partial F(k\tau)}{\partial \lambda_\ell} \qquad (11\text{-}10)$$

We assume that pulses $A(\mu_k, t - k\tau)$ with different k do not overlap, so that at any instant of time t only one of the terms of the sum (11-10) can differ from zero. In this case, the separate terms of this sum are orthogonal, and we obtain

$$\overline{D_m(t)\, D_\ell(t)} = \sum_{k=-T/2\tau}^{(T/2\tau)-1} \overline{[\partial A(\mu_k, t - k\tau)/\partial \mu_k]^2} \frac{\partial F(k\tau)}{\partial \lambda_m} \frac{\partial F(k\tau)}{\partial \lambda_\ell} \qquad (11\text{-}11)$$

Moreover, clearly

$$\overline{[\partial A(\mu_k, t - k\tau)/\partial \mu_k]^2} = \overline{[\partial A(\mu_k, t)/\partial \mu_k]^2} = \overline{A'^2_\mu(\mu, t)} \qquad (11\text{-}12)$$

We shall assume for simplicity that this quantity does not depend on the value of μ; this is the case, e.g., in all the examples analyzed in Part III. In the cases where this quantity depends on the value of μ, the intensity of the noise process at the receiver output will depend on the modulating waveform F(t), and the calculation of this intensity becomes complicated. However, if in this case we look for the noise intensity at the receiver output for F(t) = 0, then the results of the calculations are valid; we need only replace the expression

$A'^2_\mu(\mu, t)$ by its value for $\mu = 0$. Taking account of (11-12), we obtain

$$\overline{D_m(t)\, D_\ell(t)} = A'^2_\mu(\mu, t) \sum_{k=-T/2\tau}^{(T/2\tau)-1} \frac{\partial F(k\tau)}{\partial \lambda_m} \frac{\partial F(k\tau)}{\partial \lambda_\ell} \tag{11-13}$$

Moreover, from Eq. (9-1) we obtain

$$\frac{\partial F(k\tau)}{\partial \lambda_{2i}} = \sqrt{2} \cos \frac{2\pi}{T}\, ik\tau \tag{11-14}$$

$$\frac{\partial F(k\tau)}{\partial \lambda_{2i-1}} = \sqrt{2} \sin \frac{2\pi}{T}\, ik\tau$$

Substituting these expressions into the sum (11-13), we obtain

$$\overline{D_m(t)\, D_\ell(t)} = 0 \qquad \text{for} \quad m \neq \ell$$

$$\overline{D^2_\ell(t)} = \frac{1}{\tau}\, T\, \overline{A'^2_\mu(\mu, t)} \tag{11-15}$$

Thus, according to Eq. (9-27), at the output of the ideal receiver, in addition to the reproduced waveform F(t), we obtain fluctuation noise added to it, with a spectrum equal to

$$\sigma^* = \frac{\sigma\sqrt{\tau}}{\sqrt{T\, \overline{A'^2_\mu(\mu, t)}}} \tag{11-16}$$

We know from Section 6-6 that when a parameter μ is transmitted using the signal $A(\mu, t)$, we obtain the least possible mean square error δ_{mm}, given by Eq. (6-40), when reception is with an ideal receiver. It follows from the form of these equations that the noise intensity at the receiver output can be expressed as

$$\sigma^{*2} = 2\tau\,\delta^2_{mm} \tag{11-17}$$

We see that the normal fluctuation noise which the added noise produces at the output of the ideal receiver has uniform intensity, just as in the case of the direct modulation methods. The intensity of this noise becomes larger when the minimum mean square error δ_{mm} for transmission of the instantaneous values $F(k\tau)$ of the transmitted (modulating) waveform becomes larger. Thus, the problem of raising the optimum noise immunity for the pulse modulation system reduces to decreasing the minimum mean square error obtained in transmitting the instantaneous values. All that was said about this in Part III is applicable in the present case. By decreasing τ, i.e., by decreasing the number of signal pulses, we can decrease σ^*, but the average signal power is thereby increased.

In what follows, we shall need to know the effective value U_{eo} of the signal when $F(t) = 0$, which for the pulse modulation system is given by

$$U_{eo}^2 = \overline{A_F^2(t)} = \overline{\left[\sum_{k=-T/2\tau}^{(T/2\tau)-1} A(0, t - k\tau)\right]^2} = \sum_{k=-T/2\tau}^{(T/2\tau)-1} \overline{A^2(0, t - k\tau)}$$

$$= \frac{1}{\tau} T \overline{A^2(0,t)} \qquad (11\text{-}18)$$

according to Eq. (11-3). Here we used the fact that the waveforms of the separate pulses do not overlap, and are therefore orthogonal as this implies.

11-4 Noise immunity of the receiver analyzed in section 11-2

In this section we investigate the noise immunity of the pulse modulation receiver which uses the principle of operation studied in Section 11-2, and we compare this noise immunity with the optimum noise immunity. In doing this, we assume that the first part of the receiver in question, which reproduces the instantaneous values from the received signal, operates ideally. In Section 6-5, it was shown that when weak noise is added to the signal, the transmitted quantities are reproduced by the ideal receiver with errors which in the given case, according to Eqs. (6-29), (6-36) and (6-38), are for the k-th pulse equal to

$$\delta_k = \overline{L_k(t)\, W_{\mu,\nu}(t)} = \delta_{mm}\, \theta_k \qquad (11\text{-}19)$$

where

$$L_k(t) = A'_\mu(\mu, t - k\tau) / \overline{A'^2_\mu(\mu, t - k\tau)}$$

θ_k is a normal random variable, and

$$\delta_{mm} = \frac{\sigma}{\sqrt{2T\, \overline{A'^2_\mu(\mu, t - k\tau)}}}$$

is the mean square error with the ideal receiver. Since the pulses which are used to transmit the various instantaneous values are by hypothesis non-overlapping, the $L_k(t)$ with different indices are mutually orthogonal. Therefore, according to (2-60) and (2-61), the θ_k are mutually independent. Moreover, since we assumed in Section 11-3 that $\overline{A'^2_\mu(\mu, t - k\tau)}$ does not depend on μ, we find that the quantities $\overline{L_k^2(t)}$ and therefore also δ_{mm} do not depend on μ.

Due to the action of noise, the receiver reproduces the values $F(k\tau) + \delta_{mm}\,\theta_k$

instead of the instantaneous values $F(k\tau)$. According to Section 11-2, in order to use these values to restore the waveform $F(t)$, we form a system of short pulses, which in this case has the form

$$\sum_{k=-T/2\tau}^{(T/2\tau)-1} [F(k\tau) + \delta_{mm}\theta_k]\ \Phi(t - k\tau)$$

$$= \sum_{k=-T/2\tau}^{(T/2\tau)-1} F(k\tau)\ \Phi(t - k\tau) + \delta_{mm} \sum_{k=-T/2\tau}^{(T/2\tau)-1} \theta_k\ \Phi(t - k\tau) \qquad (11\text{-}20)$$

If in this expression we leave only oscillations with frequencies less than $1/2\tau$, then, as shown in Section 11-2, the first term of this expression equals the quantity $d_o F(t)$, where d_o is some constant. We now show that under these conditions, the second term is normal fluctuation noise with intensity equal to

$$\sqrt{2\tau}\,\delta_{mm}\, d_o \qquad (11\text{-}21)$$

for the frequencies from 0 to $1/2\tau$. We first find the cosine component of the second term at frequency n/T; it equals

$$C_n = \frac{2}{T} \int_{-T/2}^{+T/2} \delta_{mm} \sum_{k=-T/2\tau}^{(T/2\tau)-1} \theta_k\ \Phi(t - k\tau) \cos \frac{2\pi}{T} nt\ dt$$

$$= \frac{2\delta_{mm}}{T} \sum_{k=-T/2\tau}^{(T/2\tau)-1} \theta_k \int_{-T/2}^{+T/2} \Phi(t - k\tau) \cos \frac{2\pi}{T} nt\ dt$$

Since $\Phi(t - k\tau)$ is different from zero only in the immediate neighborhood of $t = k\tau$, we have

$$\int_{-T/2}^{+T/2} \Phi(t - k\tau) \cos \frac{2\pi}{T} nt\ dt = a \cos \frac{2\pi}{T} nk\tau$$

where

$$a = \int_{-T/2}^{+T/2} \Phi(t - k\tau)\ dt = \int_{-T/2}^{+T/2} \Phi(t)\ dt \qquad (11\text{-}22)$$

so that

$$C_n = \frac{2\delta_{mm}}{T} a \sum_{k=-T/2\tau}^{(T/2\tau)-1} \theta_k \cos \frac{2\pi}{T} nk\tau$$

According to Eq. (2-74), taking into consideration the fact that the θ_k are independent normal random variables, we obtain

$$C_n = \frac{2\delta_{mm}}{T} a\sqrt{T/2\tau}\, \theta_{cn} \tag{11-23}$$

where θ_{cn} is a normal random variable, inasmuch as

$$\sum_{k=-T/2\tau}^{(T/2\tau)-1} \cos^2 \frac{2\pi}{T} nk\tau = \sum_{k=-T/2\tau}^{(T/2\tau)-1} \left(\frac{1}{2} + \frac{1}{2} \cos \frac{4\pi}{T} nk\tau\right) = \frac{T}{2\tau}$$

since the sum of cosines is zero for $n/T < 1/2\tau$. In the same way, the amplitude of the sine component at frequency n/T is equal to

$$S_n = \frac{2\delta_{mm}}{T} a \sqrt{T/2\tau}\, \theta_{sn} \tag{11-24}$$

Using Section 2-5, it is not hard to show that the random variables $\theta_{c1}, \theta_{s1}, \theta_{c2}, \theta_{s2}, \ldots$ are mutually independent.

We now find the quantity d_o which is the constant component of the series (11-6). It equals

$$d_o = \frac{1}{T} \int_{-T/2}^{+T/2} \sum_{k=-T/2\tau}^{(T/2\tau)-1} \Phi(t - k\tau)\, dt = \frac{1}{T} \frac{T}{\tau} a \tag{11-25}$$

whence $a = \tau d_o$. Bearing in mind all that has been said, and retaining in the second term of the waveform (11-20) only components with frequencies less than $1/2\tau$, we obtain the waveform

$$W_{1,(T/2\tau)-1}(t) = \delta_{mm} d_o \sqrt{2\tau/T} \sum_{n=1}^{(T/2\tau)-1} \left(\theta_{cn} \cos \frac{2\pi}{T} nt + \theta_{sn} \sin \frac{2\pi}{T} nt\right) \tag{11-26}$$

which, as follows from a comparison with Eq. (2-54), is the normal fluctuation noise with the constant intensity equal to (11-21), as was to be proved.

If we now choose the gain of the receiver in such a way as to make $F(t)$ the waveform at its output in the absence of noise, then, clearly, the additional waveform which is added to the output waveform in the presence of noise is the normal fluctuation process with intensity

$$\sigma^* = \sqrt{2\tau}\ \delta_{mm} \qquad (11\text{-}27)$$

Comparing this result with that obtained in Section 11-3 for the optimum noise immunity, we arrive at the conclusion that the means of reception analyzed in Section 11-2 provides the optimum noise immunity, if in it we use the ideal receiver to reproduce the instantaneous transmitted values. In the case where a nonideal receiver is used for this purpose, the mean square error δ_m in reproducing the instantaneous values is larger than δ_{mm}, and the intensity of the noise at the receiver output is increased by the same amount as compared with the ideal case.

11-5 Optimum noise immunity for pulse amplitude modulation

For pulse amplitude modulation the separate pulses are given by Eq. (7-1). According to Eqs. (7-2) and (11-17), the noise intensity at the output of the ideal receiver is

$$\sigma^{*2} = \frac{\sigma}{T\ \overline{B^2(t)}} \qquad (11\text{-}28)$$

For convenience in comparing this with other kinds of modulation, we replace $\overline{B^2(t)}$ in this formula by the effective value of the signal. According to Eqs. (7-1) and (11-18), we obtain

$$U_{eo}^2 = \frac{T\ \overline{A^2(0,t)}}{\tau} = \frac{T\ \overline{B^2(t)}}{\tau} \qquad (11\text{-}29)$$

Substituting this quantity in Eq. (11-28), we obtain

$$\sigma^* = \frac{\sigma}{U_{eo}} \qquad (11\text{-}30)$$

We now compare this value of the intensity of the noise process at the output of the ideal receiver with the same quantity for ordinary amplitude modulation, discussed in Section 10-3 and characterized by Eq. (10-8). As the comparison shows, the noise intensity at the output, and therefore the optimum noise immunity, of the two systems is the same. We saw in Section 10-5 that the optimum noise immunity for amplitude modulation in the presence of weak noise can be realized using the ordinary receiver. Therefore, the pulse amplitude modulation system cannot provide better noise protection for the same average signal power than ordinary amplitude modulation, regardless of the receiver, at least for weak noise and under the conditions for which the method of reception described in Section 10-5 is realizable.

11-6 Optimum noise immunity for pulse time modulation

Let the signal in this case be given by Eq. (7-9). According to Eqs. (7-11) and (11-17), the noise intensity at the output of the ideal receiver is equal to

$$\sigma^{*2} = \frac{24\tau\sigma^2}{\pi\tau_o^2\Omega U_o^2} \qquad (11\text{-}31)$$

We now express this quantity in terms of U_{eo}^2, using Eq. (11-18). In this case

$$T\,\overline{A^2(\mu,t)} = \frac{\pi}{2\Omega} U_o^2$$

whence

$$U_{em}^2 = U_{eo}^2 = U_e^2 = \frac{\pi U_o^2}{2\Omega\tau} \qquad (11\text{-}32)$$

Taking account of this value, we obtain

$$\sigma^{*2} = \frac{12\sigma^2}{\Omega^2\tau_o^2 U_e^2} \qquad (11\text{-}33)$$

for the case of pulse time modulation. It is clear that the noise immunity increases when we increase the time shift τ_o of the modulated pulses. Since this time cannot exceed τ, we have $\tau_o < \tau < 1/2f_m$, where f_m is the maximum frequency of the transmitted waveform. We give τ_o its maximum possible value by setting $\tau_o = 1/2f_m$. In practice, τ_o is always somewhat less than this value, so that for this value of τ_o we obtain a somewhat larger value of the noise immunity, which, according to Eq. (11-33) is determined by the quantity

$$\sigma^{*2} = \frac{48f_m^2\sigma^2}{\Omega^2 U_e^2} = \frac{12}{\pi^2}(2\pi f_m/\Omega)^2 \frac{\sigma^2}{U_e^2} = 1.21(2\pi f_m/\Omega)^2 \frac{\sigma^2}{U_e^2} \qquad (11\text{-}34)$$

The quantity $(2\pi f_m/\Omega)$ shows how many times smaller the bandwidth $2f_m$ which the signal occupies for ordinary amplitude modulation is than the bandwidth Ω/π it occupies for pulse time modulation. Comparing this formula with Eq. (10-8) which characterizes ordinary amplitude modulation, we see that the noise intensity at the output of the ideal receiver for pulse time modulation is approximately as many times less than that for amplitude modulation, as the bandwidth occupied by pulse time modulation is greater than that occupied by amplitude modulation. According to Eq. (2-57), for pulse time modulation with bandwidth 0 to f_m, the effective value of the noise voltage at the output of the ideal receiver is

$$\sqrt{E\ \overline{W^2_{1,(T/2\tau)-1}(t)}} = \sigma^* \sqrt{f_m} = 1.1\ \frac{2\pi f_m^{3/2}}{\Omega}\ \frac{\sigma}{U_e} \qquad (11\text{-}35)$$

11-7 Optimum noise immunity for pulse frequency modulation

For this kind of modulation, the pulses are given by Eq. (7-37). According to Eq. (7-40), the noise intensity at the output of the ideal receiver is

$$\sigma^{*2} = \frac{24\,\tau\,\sigma^2}{\Omega^2\,U_o^2\,\tau_o^3} \qquad (11\text{-}36)$$

By Eqs. (7-39) and (11-18), the effective value of the signal waveform is in this case

$$U^2_{eo} = U^2_{em} = U^2_e = \frac{U_o^2\,\tau_o}{2\tau}$$

since

$$T\ \overline{A^2(\mu, t)} = \frac{1}{2}\,U_o^2\,\tau_o$$

Substituting this quantity in Eq. (11-36), we obtain

$$\sigma^{*2} = \frac{12\,\sigma^2}{\Omega^2\,\tau_o^2\,U_e^2} \qquad (11\text{-}37)$$

Comparing this formula with Eq. (11-33), we see that they are completely identical. In both formulas Ω/π is approximately the bandwidth occupied by the signal, and τ_o is approximately the time required to transmit one pulse. Therefore, all conclusions concerning this modulation system coincide with the conclusions concerning the pulse time modulation analyzed in the preceding section. In this case, we must also try to make τ_o as large a quantity as possible. As before, the maximum possible value is $\tau_o = \tau$. Eq. (11-34) and the deductions from it are also valid in this case. Of course, the methods of combined modulation discussed in Section 7-9 are also available to raise the noise immunity in the presence of weak noise.

CHAPTER 12

INTEGRAL MODULATION SYSTEMS

12-1 Definition

Systems such that the integral $\int F(t)\,dt$, rather than the transmitted waveform $F(t)$ itself, enters the analytic expression for the signal, will be called integral modulation systems. A well known example of such modulation is frequency modulation, where the frequency of the transmitted waveform can be written as

$$\omega = \omega_o + \Omega F(t)$$

where Ω is the frequency deviation and $F(t)$ is the transmitted waveform, the value of which by hypothesis varies within the range ± 1. As is well known, the analytic expression for the signal with this frequency is

$$A_F(t) = U_o \cos[\omega_o t + \Omega \int F(t)\,dt] \tag{12-1}$$

It is apparent from this formula that this modulation differs from phase modulation, given by Eq. (10-10), in that it contains the integral of the function instead of the function itself. It is clear that very many different types of integral modulation can be produced. To do so, it is enough to replace $F(t)$ in any formula for the signal in direct modulation by the integral of $F(t)$.

12-2 Optimum noise immunity for integral modulation systems

For the integral modulation system, the signal can be written as

$$A_F(t) = A[\int F(t)\,dt,\ t] = A[\Psi, t] \tag{12-2}$$

where

$$\Psi = \int F(t)\,dt = \int \sum_{i=i_1}^{i_2} (\lambda_{2i-1}\sqrt{2}\sin\frac{2\pi}{T}it + \lambda_{2i}\sqrt{2}\cos\frac{2\pi}{T}it)\,dt$$

$$= \sum_{i=i_1}^{i_2}\left(-\frac{T\lambda_{2i-1}}{2\pi i}\sqrt{2}\cos\frac{2\pi}{T}it + \frac{T\lambda_{2i}}{2\pi i}\sqrt{2}\sin\frac{2\pi}{T}it\right) \tag{12-3}$$

It follows from this that

$$D_\ell(t) = \frac{\partial A_F(t)}{\partial \lambda_\ell} = \frac{\partial A_F(t)}{\partial \Psi} \frac{\partial \Psi}{\partial \lambda_\ell}$$

where

$$\frac{\partial \Psi}{\partial \lambda_{2i-1}} = -\frac{T}{2\pi i} \sqrt{2} \cos \frac{2\pi}{T} it$$

$$\frac{\partial \Psi}{\partial \lambda_{2i}} = \frac{T}{2\pi i} \sqrt{2} \sin \frac{2\pi}{T} it$$

Therefore, as in Section 10-2

$$\overline{D^2_{2i-1}(t)} = \overline{D^2_{2i}(t)} = \left(\frac{T}{2\pi i}\right)^2 \overline{[\partial A_F(t)/\partial \Psi]^2}$$

and

$$\overline{D_k(t)\, D_\ell(t)} = 0, \qquad k \neq \ell$$

In proving these statements, it was assumed that the function $[\partial A_F(t)/\partial \Psi]^2$ contains only sinusoidal components with frequencies higher than $2i_2/T$, i.e., higher than twice the maximum frequency contained in the transmitted waveform F(t). Thus, the conditions (9-15) are valid for integral modulation systems, and we can use Eq. (9-27). Therefore, for these systems the noise intensity at the output of the ideal receiver is

$$\sigma^*\left(\frac{i}{T}\right) = \frac{\sigma}{\sqrt{\overline{[\partial A_F(t)/\partial \Psi]^2}}} \frac{2\pi i}{T} \tag{12-4}$$

so that the noise intensity at frequency f is

$$\sigma^*(f) = \frac{\sigma}{\sqrt{\overline{[\partial A_F(t)/\partial \Psi]^2}}} 2\pi f \tag{12-5}$$

As we see from this formula, in integral modulation systems the noise intensity at the output of the ideal receiver increases in proportion to the frequency, as opposed to the modulation systems studied earlier. According to Eq. (D-9), the effective value of the noise process at the output is

$$\sqrt{E\,\overline{W^{*2}(t)}} = \sqrt{\int_0^\infty \sigma^{*2}(f)\,df} = \frac{2\pi\sigma}{\sqrt{\overline{[\partial A(t)/\partial\Psi]^2}}}\sqrt{\int_0^{f_m} f^2\,df}$$

$$= \frac{2\pi}{\sqrt{3}}\,\frac{\sigma f_m^{3/2}}{\sqrt{\overline{[\partial A_F(t)/\partial\Psi]^2}}} \qquad (12\text{-}6)$$

12-3 Optimum noise immunity for frequency modulation

We now apply the formula obtained in the preceding section to the case of frequency modulation. For frequency modulation, the signal can be represented by Eq. (12-1). Thus, applying the notation of the preceding section, we obtain

$$A_F(t) = U_o \cos(\omega_o t + \Omega\Psi)$$

$$\partial A_F(t)/\partial\Psi = -U_o\Omega \sin(\omega_o t + \Omega\Psi)$$

As can be seen, the square of the last waveform does not contain any low frequencies if ω_o is sufficiently large. Moreover

$$\overline{[\partial A_F(t)/\partial\Psi]^2} = \frac{1}{2} U_o^2 \Omega^2$$

whence, according to Eq. (12-5), we have

$$\sigma^*(f) = \frac{\sqrt{2}\,\sigma}{U_o}\,\frac{2\pi f}{\Omega} \qquad (12\text{-}7)$$

For this kind of modulation, the effective value of the signal equals

$$U_e^2 = U_{eo}^2 = U_{em}^2 = \frac{1}{2} U_o^2$$

Therefore, in this case

$$\sigma^*(f) = \frac{2\pi f}{\Omega}\,\frac{\sigma}{U_e} \qquad (12\text{-}8)$$

According to Eq. (12-6), for this modulation the effective noise voltage at the output of the ideal receiver is

$$\sqrt{E\,\overline{W^{*2}(t)}} = \frac{2\pi}{\sqrt{3}}\,\frac{f_m^{3/2}}{\Omega}\,\frac{\sigma}{U_e} = 0.578\,\frac{2\pi f_m^{3/2}}{\Omega}\,\frac{\sigma}{U_e} \qquad (12\text{-}9)$$

Comparing this kind of modulation with pulse time modulation and pulse frequency modulation with optimum noise immunity given by Eq. (11-34), we see that at the highest frequency f_m the noise intensity at the output of the ideal receiver is approximately the same in both cases. In the case of frequency modulation, when the frequency is decreased, the noise intensity decreases, as opposed to the pulse systems, where it remains constant. This gives approximately twice as small a value of the effective noise voltage at the output of the ideal receiver for frequency modulation as compared with pulse modulation, as follows by comparing Eqs. (11-35) and (12-9). A comparison of the noise immunity of the ideal receiver with the noise immunity of the real receiver which is usually used shows that the noise immunities are the same for frequency modulation in the presence of weak noise.

CHAPTER 13

EVALUATION OF THE INFLUENCE OF STRONG NOISE ON THE TRANSMISSION OF WAVEFORMS

13-1 General considerations

In this chapter, we show how to evaluate the optimum noise immunity of systems which are used to transmit waveforms, in the presence of strong noise. A precise evaluation of the influence of noise in this case is often very difficult. The noise process at the receiver output may not even be normal fluctuation noise, and may depend on the transmitted waveform. However, it is not hard to obtain an approximate evaluation of the influence of strong noise by using the maximum discrimination of the transmitted waveforms, which cannot be exceeded with any receiver, for the given means of transmission and the given noise intensity.

13-2 Maximum discrimination of transmitted waveforms

Let a waveform $F_1(t)$ (a sound wave, say) be transmitted; in this case the transmitted signal is $A_{F_1}(t)$. Let the noise $W_{\mu,\nu}(t)$ be added to this signal, with the result that the receiver does not reproduce the waveform $F_1(t)$ at its output, but another waveform, which is a distortion of $F_1(t)$ produced by the noise. If the waveform $F_2(t)$ was transmitted instead of $F_1(t)$, then the transmitted signal would be $A_{F_2}(t)$. In this case, due to the action of noise, the waveform at the receiver would look like a perturbed version of the waveform $F_2(t)$. The amount of distortion produced by the noise can be evaluated as the probability that by using the waveform reproduced by the receiver (a sound wave in this case) we correctly determine whether $F_1(t)$ or $F_2(t)$ was sent. This probability can be obtained experimentally, e. g. , by using the following articulation experiment, which is suitable for the case of telephony: Sometimes let the sound waveform $F_1(t)$ be sent, and other times let the waveform $F_2(t)$ be sent, in an order which is unknown at the receiving end, but in such a way that on the average both waveforms are sent equally often. Suppose that at the receiving end a listener writes down each time which waveform, in his opinion, was sent. Obviously, in some cases he will write down the correct answer, and in other cases the incorrect answer, as can be ascertained subsequently. Then, for a sufficiently large number of trials, the number of correctly chosen sound waveforms divided by the total number of transmitted sound waveforms equals the desired probability.

The maximum possible value of this probability for a given means of transmission, i. e. for given signals $A_{F_1}(t)$ and $A_{F_2}(t)$, can easily be found theoretically. In fact, in Chapter 4 we found the probability that the ideal receiver correctly decides which of two signals known in advance was sent, when noise is added to the signal. Also we showed that no other means of reception can provide a larger value of this probability. If we correctly determine which of two waveforms $F_1(t)$ and $F_2(t)$ was sent, by using the waveform at the receiver output, we thereby determine which of the signals $A_1(t)$ and $A_2(t)$ was sent. Therefore, the probability that we correctly decide which of the waveforms $F_1(t)$ or $F_2(t)$ was sent, by using the waveform at the receiver output, which is distorted by noise, cannot be greater than the probability that the ideal receiver correctly discriminates between the signals $A_{F_1}(t)$ and $A_{F_2}(t)$. According to Section 4-1, this latter probability is equal to

$$1 - P_E = 1 - V(\alpha) \tag{13-1}$$

where

$$\alpha = \frac{1}{\sigma}\sqrt{\frac{T}{2}\,[A_{F_1}(t) - A_{F_2}(t)]^2} \tag{13-2}$$

In this way, we can evaluate the discrimination which cannot be exceeded, given the waveform, the modulation method, and the noise intensity. By this means, it is clear that we can also determine in many cases how close the given receiver is to being ideal in the presence of strong noise. In fact, if it turns out that the probability determined experimentally by the "articulation" experiment described above is close to the probability given by Eq. (13-1), this means that for the given kind of transmission, the given receiver provides almost the maximum protection against strong fluctuation noise. This also means that other receivers cannot provide more protection against this noise, when the waveforms $F_1(t)$ and $F_2(t)$ are transmitted. Clearly, the value of the method described can be determined only after applying it in practice.

In the method studied here, we use waveforms which can take on two discrete values. Of course, one can also develop a method of evaluation which uses many discrete waveforms.

13-3 Maximum discrimination for phase modulation

To illustrate the method discussed in the preceding section, we apply it to the special case of phase modulation. In order to test the influence of noise, we transmit either the waveform

$$\begin{aligned} F_1(t) &= \sin \Omega t, && \text{for} \quad -\tau_o/2 \le t \le \tau_o/2 \\ F_1(t) &= 0, && \text{for} \quad t < -\tau_o/2 \quad \text{and} \quad t > \tau_o/2 \end{aligned} \tag{13-3}$$

or the absence of any waveform, i.e.

$$F_2(t) = 0 \tag{13-4}$$

Suppose we study phase modulation, for which the transmitted signal equals

$$A_F(t) = U_o \cos [\omega_o t + mF(t)] \tag{13-5}$$

Then, in our case, we obtain

$$A_{F_1}(t) = U_o \cos [\omega_o t + m \sin \Omega t] \quad \text{for} \quad -\tau_o/2 \leq t \leq \tau_o/2 \tag{13-6}$$

$$A_{F_1}(t) = U_o \cos \omega_o t \qquad \text{for } t < -\tau_o/2 \text{ and } t > \tau_o/2 \tag{13-7}$$

and

$$A_{F_2}(t) = U_o \cos \omega_o t \tag{13-8}$$

Substituting these expressions into (13-2), and assuming for simplicity that $\omega_o \gg \Omega$ and that $\Omega\tau_o/\pi$ is an integer, we obtain

$$\alpha^2 = (Q^2/\sigma^2)(1 - J_o(m)) \tag{13-9}$$

where $J_o(m)$ is the Bessel function of order zero with argument m, and

$$Q^2 = \frac{1}{2} U_o^2 \tau_o \tag{13-10}$$

Substituting this value of α into Eq. (13-1), we obtain an upper bound for the probability of correct discrimination of the waveforms $F_1(t)$ and $F_2(t)$ at the receiver output, in the presence of noise of intensity σ.

In Figure 13-1, the quantity m is plotted as abscissa, and curve 1 gives $1 - J_o(m)$ as the ordinate. The latter expression completely determines the quantity $V(\alpha)$ appearing in Eq. (13-1), if we specify the value of Q/σ. Therefore, we can also plot the value of $V(\alpha)$ along the ordinate axis in the figure, if we specify Q/σ; this has been done for the values $Q/\sigma = 1, 2, 3, 4, 6$. As the figure shows, the quantity $V(\alpha)$ increases when $m > 4$. Clearly, the reason for this is the following: For such large values of m, in order for there to be an error in interpreting the waveform $F(t)$, at the time when this waveform is expected, the noise waveform must take on a value so large that phase modulation no longer provides good protection against the noise. For such a large noise waveform, it is clear that the transmitted waveforms cannot be properly distinguished in the midst of the noise at the receiver output, regardless of the value of the modulation index m.

13-4 Maximum discrimination for weak noise

To clarify the special features which strong noise introduces, we now determine the maximum discrimination, starting from the theory derived in previous chapters for the

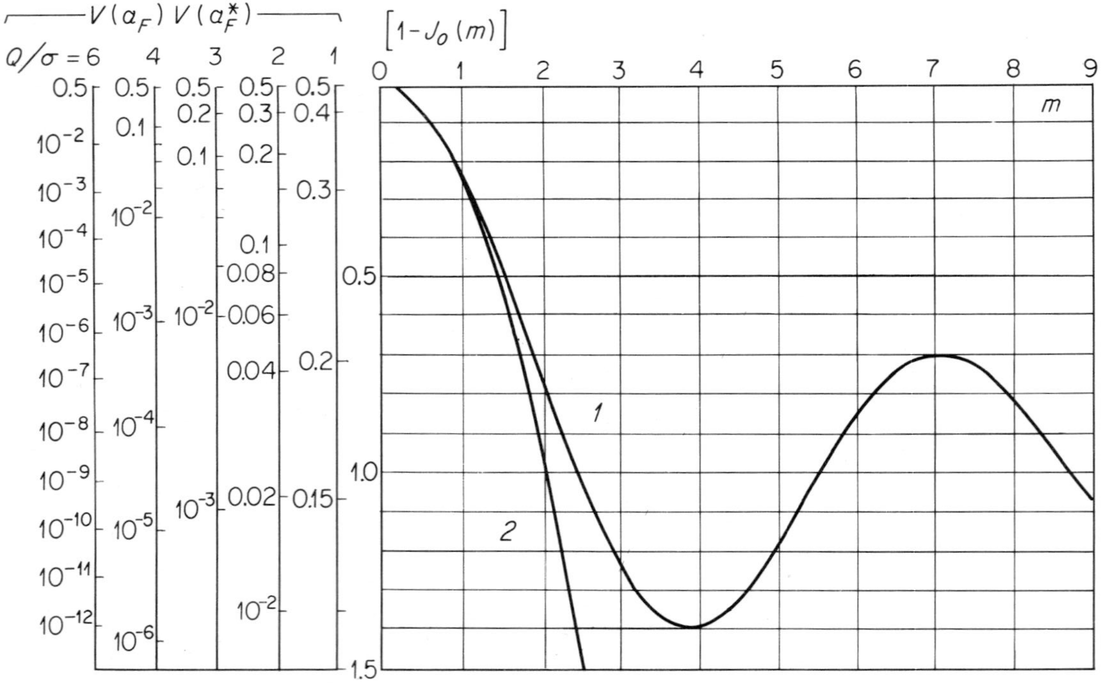

Fig. 13-1. Probability of error for transmission of a sine wave using phase modulation and the ideal receiver, for various Q/σ. Curve 1 -- exact value; curve 2 -- approximate value obtained by weak noise formula; m -- modulation index; Q^2 is defined by Eq. (13-10).

case of weak noise. When the waveform $F_1(t)$ is transmitted in the presence of weak noise, then at the output of the ideal receiver we obtain the waveform

$$F_1(t) + W^*(t) \tag{13-11}$$

and when $F_2(t)$ is transmitted, we obtain the waveform

$$F_2(t) + W^*(t) \tag{13-12}$$

where $W^*(t)$ is the normal fluctuation noise with the intensity σ^* given by Eq. (9-27). We confine ourselves to the case where σ^* does not depend on the frequency, as is always the case except for integral modulation. As shown in Section 4-1, the probability that we correctly determine which of the waveforms $F_1(t)$ or $F_2(t)$ was transmitted, using the function (13-11) and (13-12) and the ideal indicator (ideal ear), is equal to

$$1 - P_E = 1 - V(\alpha^*) \tag{13-13}$$

where

$$\alpha^* = \sqrt{\frac{T\,\overline{[F_2(t) - F_1(t)]^2}}{2\sigma^{*2}}} \tag{13-14}$$

Obviously, according to what was said in Section 13-2, the size of (13-13) cannot be greater than the probability given by Eq. (13-1). If this does not turn out to be the case, it means that the probability (13-13) was improperly calculated, which means that the assumption that the noise is sufficiently weak is not valid. In the next section, we compare this method of evaluating the maximum discrimination with the general method discussed in Section 13-2, using phase modulation as an example.

13-5 Maximum discrimination for weak noise and phase modulation

We now apply what was said in the preceding section to the case of phase modulation, which we studied in Section 13-3. Assuming that the test waveforms $F_1(t)$ and $F_2(t)$ are defined as before by Eqs. (13-3) and (13-4), and using Eqs. (13-14) and (10-11), we obtain

$$\alpha^{*2} = \frac{U_o^2 m^2}{4\sigma^2} \int_{-\tau_o/2}^{+\tau_o/2} \sin^2 \Omega t \, dt = \frac{Q^2 m^2}{4\sigma^2}$$

For simplicity, we took $\Omega\tau_o/\pi$ equal to an integer, and denoted $\tau_o U_o^2/2$ by Q^2. In Figure 13-1, curve 2 gives the dependence of the quantity $m^2/4$ on m. Thus, using this curve and giving different values to the ratio Q/σ, we can determine the quantity $V(\alpha^*)$, just as in Section 13-3 we determined the quantity $V(\alpha)$, using curve 1. As we see from the figure, the two curves are close together only when the modulation index $m < 2$. In the case where $m > 2$, the value of $V(\alpha)$ given by curve 1 is much larger than the value $V(\alpha^*)$ given by curve 2. It follows from this that the quantity (13-13), determined according to the formula derived for weak noise, is incorrect for $m > 2$, which means that the weak noise theory is not applicable in this case. Clearly, this result can be interpreted as follows: As long as the test waveform $F_1(t)$ gives a small modulation index $m < 2$, it is masked at the receiver output by noise waveforms which are small enough so that Eqs. (13-11) and (13-12) are valid. In the case where the test waveform produces a modulation index $m > 2$, it is masked at the receiver output only when the noise waveform is so large at the time when $F_1(t)$ is transmitted that Eq. (13-13) and the weak noise theory are not valid.

APPENDICES

Appendix A. The specific energy of high-frequency waveforms

As is well-known, a high-frequency signal can be represented quite generally as

$$A(t) = U_m(t) \cos [\omega_o t + \phi(t)] \qquad \text{(A-1)}$$

The specific energy of this signal is

$$Q^2 = T\,\overline{A^2(t)} = T\,\overline{U_m^2(t) \cos^2 [\omega_o t + \phi(t)]}$$

Now if we assume, as is usually the case, that ω_o is so large that the frequencies which effectively matter in the expression $\cos [2\omega_o t + 2\phi(t)]$ are all higher than the frequencies contained in the function $U_m^2(t)$, and that the constant component of $\cos [2\omega_o t + 2\phi(t)]$ can be set equal to zero for the same reason, then by Eq. (2-26), we obtain

$$Q^2 = T\,\overline{A^2(t)} = \frac{1}{2} T\,\overline{U_m^2(t)} = \frac{1}{2} \int_{-T/2}^{+T/2} U_m^2(t)\,dt \qquad \text{(A-2)}$$

Appendix B. Representation of normal fluctuation noise by two amplitude-modulated waves

We consider normal fluctuation noise with frequencies from μ/T to ν/T and constant intensity, and write

$$\ell_o = \frac{\nu + \mu}{2}, \qquad n = \frac{\nu - \mu}{2} \qquad \text{(B-1)}$$

Let ℓ_o and n be integers. Then the waveform (2-54) can be written as

$$W_{\mu,\nu}(t) = \frac{\sigma}{\sqrt{T}} \sum_{i=-n}^{n} \left[\theta_{2\ell_o+2i-1} \sin \frac{2\pi}{T} (\ell_o + i)t + \theta_{2\ell_o+2i} \cos \frac{2\pi}{T} (\ell_o + i)t \right]$$

$$= \frac{\sigma}{\sqrt{T}} \sum_{i=-1}^{n} \left\{ \theta_{2\ell_o+2i+1} \left[\sin \frac{2\pi}{T} it \cos \frac{2\pi}{T} \ell_o t + \cos \frac{2\pi}{T} it \sin \frac{2\pi}{T} \ell_o t \right] \right.$$

$$\left. + \theta_{2\ell_o+2i} \left[\cos \frac{2\pi}{T} it \cos \frac{2\pi}{T} \ell_o t - \sin \frac{2\pi}{T} it \sin \frac{2\pi}{T} \ell_o t \right] \right\} \qquad \text{(B-2)}$$

Setting $(2\pi/T)\,\ell_o = \omega_o$ and factoring out $\cos\,\omega_o t$ and $\sin\,\omega_o t$, we obtain

$$W_{\mu,\nu}(t) = \frac{\sigma}{\sqrt{T}} \sum_{i=-n}^{n} \left(\theta_{2\ell_o+2i-1} \sin\frac{2\pi}{T} it + \theta_{2\ell_o+2i} \cos\frac{2\pi}{T} it\right) \cos\,\omega_o t$$

$$+ \frac{\sigma}{\sqrt{T}} \sum_{i=-n}^{n} \theta_{2\ell_o+2i-1} \cos\frac{2\pi}{T} it - \theta_{2\ell_o+2i} \sin\frac{2\pi}{T} it)\,\sin\,\omega_o t \qquad \text{(B-3)}$$

Finally, adding terms with the same absolute value of i, we obtain

$$W_{\mu,\nu}(t) = \frac{\sigma}{\sqrt{T}} \sum_{i=1}^{n} \Big[(\theta_{2\ell_o+2i-1} - \theta_{2\ell_o-2i-1}) \sin\frac{2\pi}{T} it$$

$$+ (\theta_{2\ell_o+2i} + \theta_{2\ell_o-2i}) \cos\frac{2\pi}{T} it \Big] \cos\,\omega_o t$$

$$+ \frac{\sigma}{\sqrt{T}} \sum_{i=1}^{n} \Big[(\theta_{2\ell_o+2i-1} + \theta_{2\ell_o-2i-1}) \cos\frac{2\pi}{T} it$$

$$+ (\theta_{2\ell_o-2i} - \theta_{2\ell_o+2i}) \sin\frac{2\pi}{T} it \Big] \sin\,\omega_o t \qquad \text{(B-4)}$$

Here we have neglected the terms with $i = 0$, which is permissible if we take T large enough, since if T is increased while the frequencies μ/T and ν/T are kept the same, the number of terms will increase, while each term becomes arbitrarily small. We now introduce the notation

$$\begin{aligned}
\theta_{2\ell_o+2i-1} - \theta_{2\ell_o-2i-1} &= \sqrt{2}\;\theta''_{2i-1} \\
\theta_{2\ell_o+2i-1} + \theta_{2\ell_o-2i-1} &= \sqrt{2}\;\theta'_{2i} \\
\theta_{2\ell_o+2i} + \theta_{2\ell_o-2i} &= \sqrt{2}\;\theta''_{2i} \\
\theta_{2\ell_o-2i} - \theta_{2\ell_o+2i} &= \sqrt{2}\;\theta'_{2i-1}
\end{aligned} \qquad \text{(B-5)}$$

where, according to Section 2-5, the θ'_{2i-1}, θ''_{2i-1}, θ'_{2i}, θ''_{2i} are (mutually) independent random variables. Substituting these quantities in (B-4), we obtain

$$W_{\mu,\nu}(t) = W_{\ell_o - n,\, \ell_o + n}(t) = \sqrt{2}\, W'_{1,n}(t) \sin \omega_o t + \sqrt{2}\, W''_{1,n}(t) \cos \omega_o t \qquad \text{(B-6)}$$

where

$$W'_{1,n}(t) = \frac{\sigma}{\sqrt{T}} \sum_{i=1}^{n} (\theta'_{2i-1} \sin \frac{2\pi}{T} it + \theta'_{2i} \cos \frac{2\pi}{T} it)$$

$$W''_{1,n}(t) = \frac{\sigma}{\sqrt{T}} \sum_{i=1}^{n} (\theta''_{2i-1} \sin \frac{2\pi}{T} it + \theta''_{2i} \cos \frac{2\pi}{T} it)$$

are independent normal fluctuation processes with frequencies from zero to $\frac{n}{T} = \frac{(\nu - 2\mu)}{2T}$.

The quantity $\omega_o = \frac{2\pi}{T} \ell_o = \frac{1}{2} (\frac{2\pi}{T} \nu + \frac{2\pi}{T} \mu)$ is the mean angular frequency of the process $W_{\mu,\nu}(t)$

Appendix C. The instantaneous value of normal fluctuation noise

We now find the value of normal fluctuation noise with constant intensity at some instant of time $t = t_1$. According to Eqs. (2-54) and (2-74), we have

$$W_{\mu,\nu}(t_1) = \frac{\sigma}{\sqrt{T}} \sum_{\mu=\nu}^{\nu} (\theta_{2\ell-1} \sin \frac{2\pi}{T} \ell t_1 + \theta_{2\ell} \cos \frac{2\pi}{T} \ell t_1)$$

$$= \frac{\sigma}{\sqrt{T}} \sqrt{\sum_{\ell=\mu}^{\nu} (\sin^2 \frac{2\pi}{T} \ell t_1 + \cos^2 \frac{2\pi}{T} \ell t_1)}\ \theta_1$$

$$= \sigma \sqrt{\frac{\nu - \mu + 1}{T}}\ \theta_1 \qquad \text{(C-1)}$$

where θ_1 is a normal random variable. Introducing $f_\nu = \nu/T$ and $f_\mu = \mu/T$, the limits of the frequency band of the process under consideration, we find that for large T

$$W_{\mu,\nu}(t_1) = \sigma \sqrt{f_\nu - f_\mu}\ \theta_1 \qquad \text{(C-2)}$$

The rms value of $W_{\mu,\nu}(t_1)$ is $\sigma \sqrt{f_\nu - f_\mu}$, which agrees with (2-57).

Appendix D. Normal fluctuation noise made up of arbitrary pulses

We consider the passage of normal fluctuation noise through a linear system. Let the process $W_{1,\nu}(t)$ given by Eqs. (2-54) and (2-27), and consisting of the very short pulses (2-28), act upon the input of the system. This process can be written as

$$W_{1,\nu}(t) = \sum_{\ell=1}^{\nu} \frac{\sigma}{\sqrt{T}} (\theta_{2\ell-1} \sin \frac{2\pi}{T} \ell t + \theta_{2\ell} \cos \frac{2\pi}{T} \ell t)$$

where ν can be arbitrarily large, if the pulses are taken to be short enough. The process at the output of the system is

$$W^*(t) = \sum_{\ell=1}^{\nu} \frac{\sigma k(\ell/T)}{\sqrt{T}} \left\{ \theta_{2\ell-1} \sin\left[\frac{2\pi}{T}\ell t + \phi(\frac{\ell}{T})\right] + \theta_{2\ell} \cos\left[\frac{2\pi}{T}\ell t + \phi(\frac{\ell}{T})\right]\right\} \tag{D-1}$$

where $k(\ell/T) \exp[\, j\phi(\ell/T)\,]$ is the complex transfer coefficient of the system at the frequency ℓ/T. Expanding the sine and cosine terms in this expression, we obtain

$$W^*(t) = \sum_{\ell=1}^{\nu} \frac{\sigma k(\ell/T)}{\sqrt{T}} \Big\{ [\theta_{2\ell-1} \cos \phi(\ell/T) - \theta_{2\ell} \sin \phi(\ell/T)] \sin \frac{2\pi}{T} \ell t$$

$$+ [\theta_{2\ell-1} \sin \phi(\ell/T) + \theta_{2\ell} \cos \phi(\ell/T)] \cos \frac{2\pi}{T} \ell t \Big\} \tag{D-2}$$

According to Eqs. (2-74) and (2-75), we have

$$\theta_{2\ell-1} \cos \phi(\ell/T) - \theta_{2\ell} \sin \phi(\ell/T) = \sqrt{\cos^2 \phi(\ell/T) + \sin^2 \phi(\ell/T)}\ \theta^*_{2\ell-1} = \theta^*_{2\ell-1}$$

and

$$\theta_{2\ell-1} \sin \phi(\ell/T) + \theta_{2\ell} \cos \phi(\ell/T) = \sqrt{\sin^2 \phi(\ell/T) + \cos^2 \phi(\ell/T)}\ \theta^*_{2\ell} = \theta^*_{2\ell}$$

where $\theta^*_{2\ell-1}$ and $\theta^*_{2\ell}$ are independent normal random variables, since the condition (2-76) is satisfied, i.e.,

$$\cos \phi(\ell/T) \sin \phi(\ell/T) - \sin \phi(\ell/T) \cos \phi(\ell/T) = 0$$

Accordingly, we obtain

$$W^*(t) = \sum_{\ell=1}^{\nu} \frac{\sigma^*(\ell/T)}{\sqrt{T}} \left(\theta^*_{2\ell-1} \sin \frac{2\pi}{T} \ell t + \theta^*_{2\ell} \cos \frac{2\pi}{T} \ell t\right) \qquad \text{(D-3)}$$

where

$$\sigma^*(\ell/T) = \sigma k(\ell/T) \qquad \text{(D-4)}$$

As is evident from this expression, the phase characteristic $\phi(\ell/T)$ of the system does not affect the statistical properties of the process (D-3). We shall call the process $W^*(t)$ normal fluctuation noise with the variable intensity $\sigma^*(\ell/T) = \sigma(f)$.

The process $W_{\mu,\nu}(t)$, acting on the input of the system, consists of short pulses. Each of these pulses produces a pulse at the output of the system, with a form determined by the complex transfer coefficient $k(\ell/T) \exp[j\phi(\ell/T)]$. Thus, we can regard the process $W^*(t)$ as being formed by the superposition of a large number of similar pulses, which are randomly distributed in time. Moreover, the intensity of the process at the output of the system can be found directly from the spectral function of the output pulses. In fact, the modulus of the spectral function of the k-th output pulse is

$$|g_k(2\pi\ell/T)| = q_k\, k(\ell/T) \qquad \text{(D-5)}$$

where q_k is defined by Eq. (2-32), and is the modulus of the k-th input pulse, since the input pulses are infinitely narrow.[1] Therefore, in view of (2-39) and (D-4), we obtain

$$\sigma^{*2}(\ell/T) = \sigma^2 k^2(\ell/T) = \frac{2}{T} \sum_{k=1}^{n} q_k^2 k^2(\ell/T) = \frac{2}{T} \sum_{k=1}^{n} |g_k(2\pi\ell/T)|^2$$

Thus, the sum of a large number of pulses which are randomly distributed in time and which have (D-5) as the modulus of their spectral function, is the normal fluctuation noise (D-3) with intensity

$$\sigma^*(f) = \sqrt{\frac{2}{T} \sum_{k=1}^{n} |g_k(2\pi f)|^2} \qquad \text{(D-6)}$$

where the sum is over all pulses in the interval $-T/2, +T/2$.

It is not hard to show, by considerations similar to those given above, that the sum

$$W^{*\prime}(t) + W^{*\prime\prime}(t) + W^{*\prime\prime\prime}(t) + \cdots \qquad \text{(D-7)}$$

1. See, e.g., V. A. Kotel'nikov and A. M. Nikolayev, "Elements of Radio Engineering", Part I, Svyaz'tekhizdat (1950), Section 8-5.

of several fluctuation noises with variable intensities is also a normal fluctuation noise, with intensity given by

$$\sigma^{*2}(f) = \sigma'^2(f) + \sigma''^2(f) + \sigma'''(f) + \cdots \qquad \text{(D-8)}$$

where $\sigma'(f)$, $\sigma''(f)$, $\sigma'''(f)$, ... are the intensities of the noises $W^{*\prime}(t)$, $W^{*\prime\prime}(t)$, $W^{*\prime\prime\prime}(t)$, ... Thus, a process which consists of randomly distributed pulses with different shapes is also a normal fluctuation noise.

We now find the effective value of the normal fluctuation noise (D-3) with variable intensity. According to the theory of Fourier series, the square of the effective value is

$$\overline{W^{*2}(t)} = \sum_{\ell=1}^{\nu} \frac{\sigma^{*2}(f_\ell)}{2T} (\theta^{*2}_{2\ell-1} + \theta^{*2}_{2\ell})$$

where $f_\ell = \ell/T$. Averaging this value over an ensemble of realizations, we obtain

$$E\,\overline{W^{*2}(t)} = \sum_{\ell=1}^{\nu} \sigma^{*2}(f_\ell)\,(f_{\ell+1} - f_\ell)$$

since $E\,\theta^{*2}_{2\ell-1} = E\,\theta^{*2}_{2\ell} = 1$, and $f_{\ell+1} - f_\ell = 1/T$. As T increases, the difference $f_{\ell+1} - f_\ell$ goes to zero, and

$$E\,\overline{W^{*2}(t)} \underset{\substack{\nu\to\infty \\ T\to\infty}}{\longrightarrow} \int_0^\infty \sigma^{*2}(f)\,df$$

whence, for sufficiently large T, the effective value of the process (D-3) is

$$\sqrt{E\,\overline{W^{*2}(t)}} = \sqrt{\int_0^\infty \sigma^{*2}(f)\,df} \qquad \text{(D-9)}$$

If $\sigma^*(f)$ is zero from f_M on, we say that f_M is the upper limit of the frequency band.